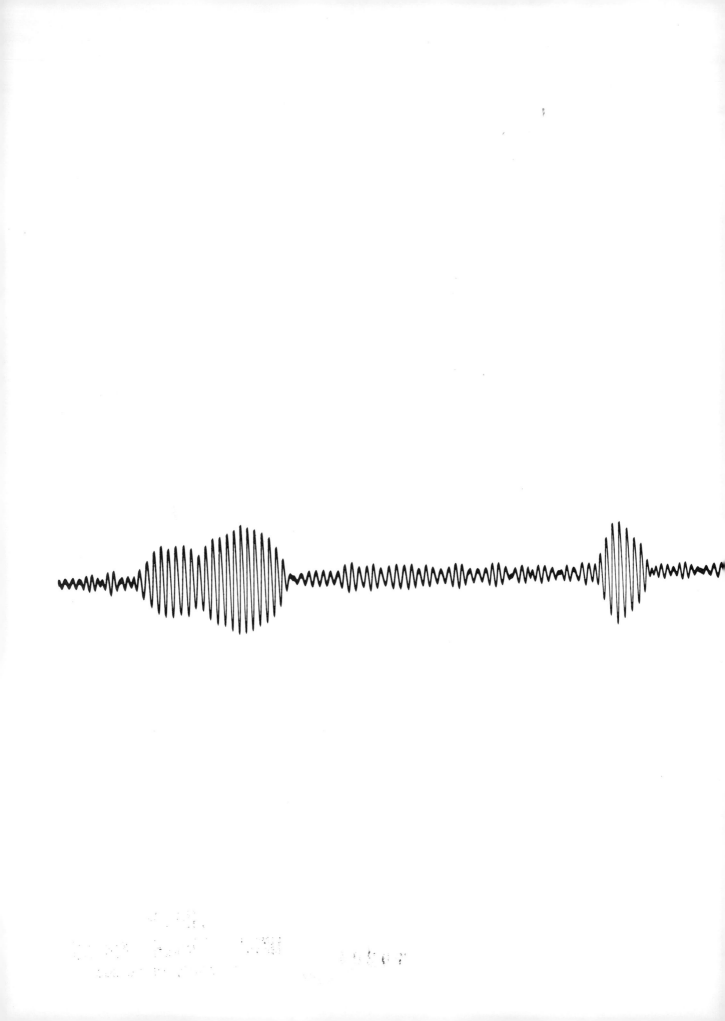

BIRD SONG: ACOUSTICS AND PHYSIOLOGY

Crawford H. Greenewalt

Smithsonian Institution Press

City of Washington

1968

Smithsonian Publication 4750
Distributed by Random House, Inc.
in the United States and Canada

Library of Congress Catalog 68–61248
Copyright © 1968 by Smithsonian Institution
All rights reserved

Designed by Crimilda Pontes
Printed in the United States of America
by Kingsport Press, Inc., Kingsport, Tennessee

PREFACE

Since I cannot qualify as an ornithologist, an acoustical physicist, or as an expert on modern instrumentation, I have had to solicit much assistance in all three categories in the preparation of this monograph. It is my pleasant duty to acknowledge that assistance here.

The signal analysis console described in chapter 2 was designed and assembled by Mr. Paul C. Hoell of the Du Pont Company's Central Research Department.

Mr. James L. Flanagan of the Bell Telephone Laboratories cheerfully undertook the task of introducing me to the complexities of acoustical physics. Many of the concepts, particularly the matched impedance of source and trachea, discussed in chapter 6, are due to him.

Professor Charles G. Sibley of Yale University has with friendly firmness kept me from ornithological errors, and has offered continual encouragement over the several years of experimentation which led to the present result.

All three gentlemen have reviewed the manuscript in detail, and their editorial and substantive comments have greatly improved my original effort.

Mr. Peter Ames, now at the Museum of Vertebrate Zoology, University of California, at Berkeley, was kind enough to provide tracheal dimensions and was also helpful in reviewing chapter 3 on the syrinx.

To avoid undue proliferation of scientific names in the text, I have used common names throughout, and list the corresponding scientific names in appendix 1.

Perhaps I should conclude by saying that this is in a sense a scientific detective story, with conclusions reached by analyzing the indirect evidence provided by the bird songs themselves. Unfortunately the criminal did not confess in the last chapter, so the evidence must remain circumstantial, and for that reason less satisfactory than direct experimental proof. Even so it has been for me a stimulating experience and I shall hope that others may be encouraged to devise methods which will show more directly whether my conclusions have been right or wrong.

Crawford H. Greenewalt
Greenville, Delaware
December 1967

CONTENTS

Chapter 1 INTRODUCTION

The song of birds, the anatomy of the vocal apparatus which produces it, the acous
tical principles involved in the act of singing, the taxonomic significance of the
anatomical structures, and more recently the behavioral aspects of song—all have
stimulated the efforts of zoologists for more than three hundred years. A mere listing
of titles from the rich and varied literature would fill a small volume.

Perhaps the earliest discovery relating to bird vocalization was the finding that
the true larynx lies deep in the thoracic cavity, not at the anterior end of the respiratory system as it does in humans, and for that matter in all mammals. This
discovery must indeed be lodged in antiquity for it depends on the rather gruesome
observation that ducks, geese, and chickens will continue their cries for some time
after their heads have been cut off. Aldrovandus (1600) appears to have been the
first to record this fact in his ornithological treatise, thus marking the beginning of the
scientific literature on bird song. Birds have a larynx located, as in mammals, at
the anterior end of the trachea, but it appears to have little if anything to do with the
production of song. To avoid confusion between the "upper" and "lower" larynx,
Huxley (1871, p. 103) suggested the term "syrinx" for the true song-producing
organs. And so the terminology has crystallized—a "larynx" serving principally to
close off the respiratory system during the feeding process, and a "syrinx" located
at the junction of trachea and bronchi which is the source of vocalization or song.
It should be noted that in most cases the syrinx comprises two completely separate
sound sources, one in each bronchus. Here again birds are unique in possessing twin
sound-producing organs in contrast to the single source characteristic of mammals.

The syringeal anatomy of several hundred species has been described. Unfortunately it is not easy to make the transition from an anatomical structure, no matter how detailed, to a description of its functional operation. Because of this difficulty we still have little understanding of the acoustical and physiological processes involved in the singing of birds. This has not been for want of effort—many papers have been written on the subject—it is simply a reflection of the difficulty of doing much more than intelligent speculation with the tools for experimentation heretofore available.

Milne-Edwards (1876, p. 623) said:

Up to this time the theory of the phonation of birds has not been established in a satisfactory manner . . . . The voice as we understand it is a resultant arising out of the interaction of various phenomena; the apparatus which produces it resembles in no way the wind instruments used by musicians, or whose sounds have been studied by physicists.

We can make no more satisfactory statement today.

A review of the literature on the acoustics of bird vocalization indicates that two principal theories have been put forward. One of these likens the production of bird song to the playing of a wind instrument such as a clarinet, oboe, or trombone. Here the vibrating membranes in the syrinx comprise the reed, or the lips of the trombonist, and the trachea is the tube which controls the pitch of the song. The second theory presumes bird song to be produced by a mechanism similar to that involved in human speech. Here the vibrating membranes are analogous to the glottis, and the trachea becomes equivalent to the oral cavities in modulating the glottal sounds.

In the paragraphs which follow, the conclusions reached by the principal authors who have studied the subject are cited as they have stated them in their original papers (the translations are mine).

Hérissant (1753, p. 291):

For certain birds, such as the goose, etc., there are four of these membranes, shaped and arranged much like the double reed of the oboe. These four membranes are arranged two by two, forming, as one sees, two separate membranous reeds . . . .

Cuvier (1805, p. 462):

It follows from what I have shown above, that sound is produced in the vocal organs of birds in the same manner as in wind instruments, such as horns and trumpets, or in the type of organ pipe known as 'jeux d'anche'; that it is modified, as to tone, by the same three methods we employ in these instruments, that is to say

1. By variations in the glottis, corresponding to those of the lips of the player, or to those of the copper reed of the 'jeux d'anches.'

2. By variations in the length of the trachea, which correspond to valved horns, or to the different lengths of organ pipes.

3. By the contraction or expansion of the upper glottis, which corresponds to the hand of the horn player, and to the closure or to the tubes of organ pipes.

Cuvier (1805, p. 491):
I think it can be concluded that the vocal organ of birds is a true wind instrument of the same type as horns and trumpets; and above all that it can be compared in all particulars to the trombone.

Grützner (1879, p. 144):
I believe, therefore, that with very minor exceptions the vocalizations of birds embody the same principles as obtain for mammals; for in both cases the vocal apparatus is a membranous reed instrument—not like a flute: however in birds the 'anzatzrohr' (trachea), because of the small size of the vocal cords, the significantly high air pressure, and its relatively high elastic modulus—operates to raise or lower the pitch of the tone, which as we know is not the case for the human voice.

Häcker (1900, p. 17):
The syrinx of songbirds differs from the human vocal organs, first, by virtue of the presence of two larynges and, second, because there is above them, in the form of the trachea, a veritable 'anzatzrohr', which because of the firmness, smoothness, and the elasticity of its walls can operate to raise or lower the pitch of the tone, in the same manner as does the 'anzatzrohr' of musical instruments.

Réthi (1908, p. 109)
Hence the bird's larynx is in fact a reed pipe, and the very high whistle-like tones are due to the small size of the larynx and the vibrating folds.

Rüppell (1933, pp. 537–538):
Sound generation in the vocal organs of birds originates in the primary vibrations of the syringeal membranes. . . . From the acoustical viewpoint the vibrating structures in the syrinx of birds are to be regarded as 'membranes with induced vibrational elasticity' (Membranen mit aufgezwungenen Schwingungselastizität) whose particular vibrational behavior goes back to the principles of sound production in reed instruments.

Thorpe (1959, pp. 454–455):
It is concluded that the vocal apparatus of many of the more primitive birds acts in many respects like a wind instrument in which the resonators can be

modulated and thereby master the vibrating structure (the reed). By contrast the syrinx of many songbirds can be usually compared to the human vocal apparatus in its mode of action.

In the light of the discoveries in recent years concerning the frequencies, frequency range, and harmonic spectra occurring in bird song, the acoustical theories proposed by these authors develop serious if not fatal defects. Let us take them serially.

In musical wind instruments there is a vibrating member—the single reed of the clarinet, the double reed of oboe and bassoon, the lips of the performer for horns, trumpets, and trombones—attached to a rigid tube of metal or wood. The resonances excited in the tube when one blows into the mouthpiece are sufficiently powerful to force the vibrating source to conform its own vibrations to the harmonic spectrum characteristic of the tube. The vibrating member is in a sense passive and the pitch and timbre of the instrument are directed solely by the properties of the tube. The pitch, or fundamental, is proportional to the tube length and is controlled by opening or closing a series of holes along the bore of the tube for clarinet or oboe, by a series of valves in the trumpet, or by the slide in the trombone.

When we apply this acoustical mechanism to bird vocalization we encounter the following difficulties:

1. The frequency range in the song of many birds embraces as much as two full octaves. For the song sparrow, for example, the range extends from about 2 to 8 kc/s (kilocycles per second). The musical instrument theory would require the trachea of the song sparrow to change its length by a factor of four to encompass this range, clearly a physiological impossibility. Furthermore, we do not see birds stretching and retracting their necks when singing. Finally, the rate at which the stretching or retracting would have to be accomplished in view of the extreme rapidity with which the notes are modulated seems to present insuperable dynamic and muscular difficulties.

2. As Thorpe (1959) has pointed out, for many bird songs one observes only the fundamental frequency; higher harmonics are absent. It is a characteristic of rigid tubes that they will have resonances, if the tube is closed at one end and open at the other, at multiples of 1, 3, 5, 7, etc., of the fundamental frequency. Hence absence of harmonics is also in direct conflict with the musical instrument theory.

3. In a tube closed at one end and open at the other the length of the tube and its lowest resonance frequency are related as follows:

$$\ell = \frac{c}{4f}$$

c is the velocity of sound, 35,300 cm/sec at
  normal temperature and pressure
ℓ is the length of the tube (trachea) in centimeters
f is the first resonance frequency in cycles per second.

If now we consider the spruce grouse singing at a frequency of 85 to 90 c/s (cycles per second), the tracheal length in accordance with musical instrument theory would have to be nearly 100 cm or 40 in; the length of the bird is 15 to 17 in. The mourning dove (frequency 500 c/s) would require a tracheal length of 17.5 cm or 7 in (the length of the bird is 11 to 13 in).

At the other extreme, consider the whistling swan. The fundamental of its song is 840 c/s, corresponding to a tracheal length of 10.5 cm or 4.1 in, manifestly an impossible result in view of the size of the bird and the length of its neck. The osprey, for which the fundamental frequency is 1900 c/s, would require a trachea 4.65 cm or 1.8 in long. Consider also the Laysan albatross, singing at a frequency of nearly 3000 c/s, corresponding to a tracheal length of 3 cm, a little over an inch!

Whereas one might be able to select individual birds for which tracheal length and pitch of song correspond, there appears to be no such correlation for birds as a whole.

4. As noted above, most bird syringes contain two sound sources, one in each bronchus. Borror and Reese (1956) have shown quite conclusively for the wood thrush that portions of its song comprise two harmonically unrelated notes overlapping in time. These must arise separately, one from each sound source. Were the musical instrument theory valid such a manifestation would be impossible, for the tracheal resonances would force both sources to conform in their vibrations, thus producing a single note.

The human voice analogy poses equal difficulties, particularly for songbirds. When we speak, the source is a series of air pulses or puffs produced by the sudden opening and closing of the glottal slit. The period between pulses corresponds to the fundamental pitch of the speaking voice, roughly 120 c/s for the average male. This succession of pulses is equivalent, by Fourier analysis, to a harmonic spectrum covering a wide range of frequencies with a fundamental equal to the reciprocal of the period between pulses. The sound is then modulated in passing through the oral cavities with some frequencies suppressed and others emphasized. The result is the spoken phrase whose fine structure also provides an individually recognizable voice quality. The difficulties in applying this acoustic mechanism to bird song are the following:

1. As noted previously, many notes in bird song show no harmonics, with all of the acoustic energy concentrated at the fundamental frequency. If the harmonic spectrum produced in the syrinx should indeed embrace as wide a range as in the human glottis, one would have to attribute really extraordinary filtering efficiency to the trachea to erase all but a particular harmonic from the complex sound produced at the source.

2. Even if one assumed such an extraordinary filter performance, harmonics would still be encountered, this time at the tracheal resonances.

3. Where two voices are sounded simultaneously, as in the song of the wood thrush, one would have to assume for the trachea efficient filtration at all but two harmonically unrelated frequencies.

It seems clear that neither hypothesis can properly account for the acoustics and physiology of bird song. It must be admitted, however, that both mechanisms are superficially plausible and become untenable only in view of the detailed analysis of bird song made possible by modern instrumental techniques.

It seemed to me that more searching analysis of the songs themselves, using the sophisticated electronic measuring devices now available, should reveal more precisely the acoustical principles involved in bird song, and might also permit valid deductions as to the role played by the various anatomical structures in the syrinx and respiratory system. As justification for this viewpoint it seems in retrospect most unlikely that our present knowledge of the processes involved in human speech could have been gained through any amount of purely anatomical research. On the contrary our very great advances in this field during recent years have arisen largely out of study and analysis of the speech sounds themselves.

The present account presents the results of such an investigation of bird song. No new anatomical investigations have been made, for not only are these beyond my capabilities, but it seems clear that the anatomical studies already reported in the extensive literature are thorough, complete, and fully descriptive of the complex structure of the avian vocal organs. Here I present results of the analysis of the songs themselves, together with the deductions as to acoustical and anatomical mechanisms to which they appear to point.

Chapter 2 INSTRUMENTATION

In this chapter are presented brief descriptions of the instruments used in the present study and the function for which each is particularly suited. While the instruments are not in themselves new, they have not (with the exception of the Sonagraph) to my knowledge been used previously in the analysis of bird songs. In some cases the commercially available instruments have been modified to meet the special requirements of the present investigation. Such modifications are briefly described in appendix 2.

The Sonagraph

The visible speech sound spectrograph developed at the Bell Telephone Laboratories, commercially available under the name "Sonagraph" from the Kay Electric Company, Pine Brook, New Jersey, appears to have become the instrument of choice for ornithologists interested in the portrayal of bird song. Since the instrument has been described in detail elsewhere (Bell Telephone Laboratories, 1946), we give here only an outline of its characteristics.

The instrument comprises a recording and playback unit providing storage on a single-channel magnetic drum of a sound sample 2.4 sec in duration. A wave analyzer covering the frequency range 0–8000 c/s is utilized to scan the sample continuously, using either of two filter band-widths, nominally 45 c/s or 300 c/s. The center frequency of analysis changes linearly with time—15 c/s per revolution of the recording drum—to reproduce the sample in time-frequency coordinates during a 5-minute interval. The picture is traced on teledeltos paper with spectral intensity roughly indicated by the density of the gray-black marking. The paper is attached to a rotating cylinder mechanically centered on the axis of the magnetic recording drum.

The Sonagraph contains a special sectioning device which will show intensity-frequency relationships (intensity in db) at preselected points of time in the stored sample. The time interval analyzed is of the order of the reciprocal of the filter band-width, i.e., about 22 msec for the 45 c/s filter, 3.3 msec for the 300 c/s filter.

Three settings on the instrument, FL-1, FL-2, and HS, present a choice of fre-quency-response relationships. None of these is constant in the sense that the indi-cated intensity is the same for a given input amplitude regardless of frequency. The HS setting strongly emphasizes the higher frequency signals; the FL settings give more nearly constant frequency-amplitude relationships. Amplitude informa-tion, however, as indicated by the density of the marking is at best qualitative and it becomes almost a matter of indifference which setting is used. Because of its ap-proximate linearity, I have found the FL-1 setting most generally useful.

For the analysis of human speech the Sonagraph has been most productive and without serious deficiencies. For bird song analysis there are ambiguities associated with the interpretation of the spectra, more or less serious depending on the purpose of the experiment and on the characteristics of the particular song. These relate first to the uncertainties in amplitude or intensity information, and second to the "time delay" and "time smear" associated with band-pass filters.

It should be said that the frequency scales for the two band-pass filters are not identical. With the narrow filter, scaling off from the origin to the center of the marking gives reasonably accurate frequency data (the vertical frequency scale is roundly 0.5 in for 1 kc/s). With the wide filter, however, the marking is displaced downward so that its center line will be about 200 c/s below the true frequency[1] (figure 1). Furthermore the width of the wide filter marking will of necessity be not less than 300 c/s, and is usually more nearly 500 c/s due to the intensity-gray-scale relationship characteristic of the marking stylus and its controlling circuitry. Clearly the narrow filter should always be used if maximum precision on the frequency scale is desired.

The intensity range of the instrument will not adequately cover the full amplitude range of many bird songs. If the recording amplifier is adjusted upward to insure a readily visible marking for low amplitudes, spurious harmonics are likely to be produced (through over-recording) for the higher amplitudes. Furthermore, for bird songs containing a series of very short notes the VU meter in the instrument will not respond with sufficient rapidity, and if the amplitude is adjusted to bring the VU meter to its normal reading, over-recording and spurious harmonics are certain to result (figure 2).

---

1. I cannot explain this discrepancy. The calibrations should in theory be identical.

Owing both to the time smear and the relatively compressed time scale (1 in for 200 msec), the short notes so common in bird song appear (if at all) as blobs (narrow filter) or as fine strokes (wide filter) and it is impossible to make any precise estimate of their duration. Furthermore the indicated frequency range is likely to be exaggerated due to shock effects on the filter.

Finally, it is difficult if not impossible to interpret rapid modulations in either frequency or amplitude. With the narrow filter these appear as bands on either side of a carrier frequency (side bands), and while the period of the modulation can frequently be estimated by measuring side-band separation, one cannot tell with assurance whether it is the amplitude or frequency or both which is being modulated. Use of the wide filter does not improve matters. One sees a series of streaks from which the period of the modulation can be estimated but no further information can be readily extracted.

It is, of course, possible to extend the time scale by running the input signal at half, or at one quarter normal speed, but speed reduction produces a corresponding drop in frequency discrimination, quite serious if the wide filter is used.

In summary, the sonagram gives a useful first approximation of the song in time-frequency coordinates, and for many purposes this may well be sufficient. A good

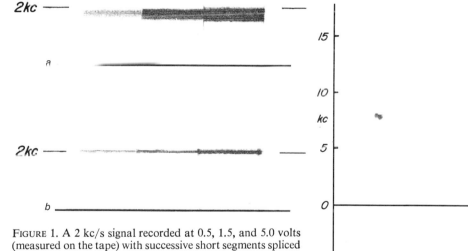

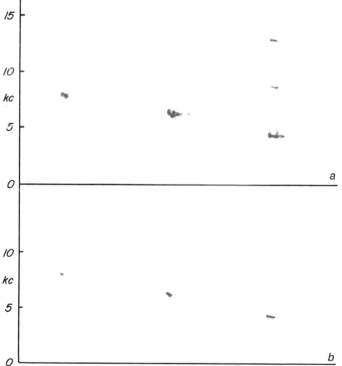

FIGURE 1. A 2 kc/s signal recorded at 0.5, 1.5, and 5.0 volts (measured on the tape) with successive short segments spliced together. Sonagrams: *a*, wide filter; *b*, narrow filter. Note the scale error, the 500 cycle width of the 5 volt wide band-pass signal, the transient effects at sudden amplitude change.

FIGURE 2. Three introductory notes from the song of a grasshopper sparrow. Sonagrams: *b*, recording volume set properly for amplitude as measured on oscilloscope, VU meter −13. *a*, recording volume increased 20 db, VU meter −3. Note spurious harmonics and tailing off of notes.

sonagram, however, is not produced automatically, and one must first understand not only the limitations of the instrument but the nature of the song being reproduced.

The Oscilloscope and its Accessories

The oscilloscope provides a precise time-amplitude array for the sound sample. Frequency information is also available, for by suitably adjusting the sweep interval one can readily count periods in a sinusoidal sound pattern and so determine frequency over any selected time period. This of course becomes difficult, in some cases impossible, if harmonics of the fundamental are present at substantial intensity. Fortunately in most bird songs, particularly those of the Oscines, harmonics are generally absent.

The oscilloscope I have used is a Tektronix type RM-504 modified to provide a take-off connection for the amplified signal. The purpose of this modification will be discussed later.

In using the oscilloscope for bird song analysis, provision must be made to permit scanning the song in predetermined time sections at any desired expansion of the time scale. For this purpose I use a dual preset digital timer, Beckman model 6005, with two independently adjustable timing circuits, each having a maximum range of 10 sec in 0.01-msec intervals. The bird song, recorded on magnetic tape, is spliced into a closed loop. For the Nagra tape recorder (q.v.) a convenient length is 28 in (an empty 5-in reel on the take-up, none on the feed) equivalent at $7\frac{1}{2}$ in/sec to a maximum of 3.6 sec of song. A magnetic pulse is impressed on the tape just before the song begins. This is done by stroking a magnetized steel pen nib several times across the tape at right angles to its long axis. The resulting strong pulse starts the timer and, when the first time setting is reached, an output pulse is produced which triggers the sweep circuit on the oscilloscope. When the second time setting is reached, the timer is automatically reset and may again be triggered by any high amplitude tape signal. To maintain timer and tape loop in synchronism, the latter circuit is set for a time interval just short of that required for a complete revolution of the tape. The timer is thus reset just before the arrival of the next starting pulse, during a silent portion of the tape loop. Suppose, for example, we wish to examine the portion of a song at one second after the starting pulse. The first timing circuit is set at one second, the second is timed to reset the starting circuit after 3.5 sec (we assume the tape is running at $7\frac{1}{2}$ in/sec) and the sweep dial on the oscilloscope is set to show the desired detail, say 1 msec/cm. Then at each round of the tape loop, that portion of the song between 1.000 and 1.010 sec after the starting pulse will be displayed on the face of the oscilloscope.

A test circuit is provided to permit precise matching of the time scale of the oscilloscope sweep to that of the digital timer. If we wish to scan the song at precisely 100-msec intervals, the two timing circuits are first set at zero. We then see a pulse on the face of the oscilloscope which is brought into coincidence with the left-hand vertical line on the oscilloscope grid by an appropriate horizontal adjustment of the signal trace. We then set the second timing circuit at 100 msec and the resulting pulse is brought into coincidence with the extreme right-hand vertical line on the grid by adjusting the variable sweep dial on the oscilloscope. By these adjustments, timer and oscilloscope are set to the same time scale. A succession of photographs[2] at 100-msec intervals can then be taken without overlap or discontinuity. The same technique can be used at any desired expansion of the time scale, for the whole, or for any portion of the song.

Figure 3 shows two such successive pictures of the oscilloscope grid. The excellent end to end match will be apparent.

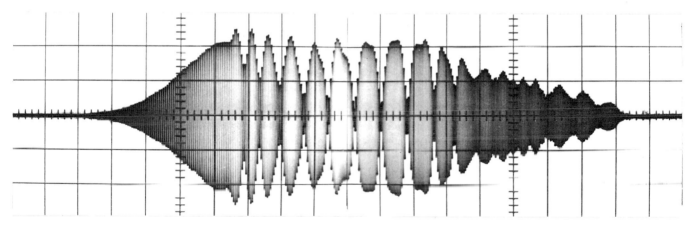

FIGURE 3. Short phrase from the song of a Lapland longspur. 5 msec per vertical division. The joint is at 50 msec from the origin.

As a signal source I have used a Nagra III-B tape recorder.[3] The fidelity of reproduction of this portable machine is equal to that of a high quality studio tape recorder, with the added advantage that use of the full tape width for the recording improves the signal/noise ratio. The precision of the timer-oscilloscope combination depends, of course, on the constancy of tape speed. In this respect the Nagra is remarkably good. For example, the starting point of the signal on the oscilloscope varies not more than $\pm 10\,\mu$ sec for a 100-msec delay and about $\pm 50\,\mu$ sec for a 1-sec delay between the starting pulse and the beginning of the portion of the song to be analyzed (figure 4). The error is negligible when one is producing a set of adjacent photographs at any useful expansion of the time scale. As we shall see further on, this

2. Where photographs are to be taken, to avoid parallax, these adjustments should be made while viewing the image on the ground glass of the camera.
3. Manufactured by Kudelski, Lausanne, Switzerland.

degree of tape-speed uniformity also permits measuring the time intervals for successive sinusoidal periods even at periods down to 100 μ sec, equivalent to a frequency of 10 kc/s.

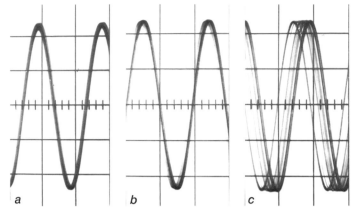

FIGURE 4. Stability of a 5 kc/s signal for 15 successive superimposed pictures on the oscilloscope. Horizontal scale 100 μ sec per major division: *a*, 1.5 c msedelay; *b*, 100 msec; *c*; 1000 msec.

Most bird song recordings contain low frequency noise (below 200–300 c/s) of sufficient amplitude to distort the amplitude-time picture of the song itself. Since the song rarely penetrates this frequency range it is convenient to insert a high pass filter with a cutoff at 300 c/s just before the oscilloscope input. For those rare occasions where the song contains frequencies below this range one can either bypass the filter or double the tape recorder speed to raise the lowest song frequencies above the cutoff point of the filter.

The output pulse corresponding to the first timer setting also operates a relay whose function we will discuss later.

In summary, the tape recorder-timer-oscilloscope combination permits one to obtain a time-amplitude display for all or part of a bird song at any desired time expansion. When permanent records are desired these can be produced from a series of photographs taken at predetermined time intervals. By bringing the time calibration of timer and oscilloscope into coincidence a series of pictures is obtained without overlap or discontinuity. One simply cuts out the grid from a series of contact prints and pastes the successive pictures end to end. For rapid inspection, Polaroid paper can be used to make the pictures. For duplication and permanence the pictures can be recorded on film as negatives for subsequent contact printing or enlargement.

The Writing Oscillograph

Even though the procedure for reproducing all or part of a bird song with oscilloscope and camera is straightforward, it is nonetheless tedious and time-consuming. Assume, for example, a song of 3-sec duration, to be shown in 15 pictures, each covering a

200-msec interval. One must take the pictures, develop the negatives, make a set of contact prints, cut out the image of the grid from each, and finally mount the prints end to end in a long strip. The process, exclusive of developing and contact printing, takes about 1½ hours.

For greater convenience I use a writing oscillograph manufactured by Consolidated Electrodynamics Corporation (Model 5-124 P4-18). In principle, the signal passes through an amplifier to a fast response galvanometer. A beam from a hydrogen arc lamp impinges on a tiny mirror on the galvanometer suspension and is reflected onto light-sensitive paper. The paper in roll form can be driven at selected speeds from 1/4 through 1, 4, 16 to 64 inches per second. The galvanometer (Model 7-361) is flat in its response to 5000 c/s. Since bird song frequencies appear rarely to exceed 10,000 c/s, one need only reduce the normal speed of the recording by one-half to obtain a faithful reproduction. Through an electronic flash attachment, timing lines can be produced across the recording paper at preselected rates of 1, 10, 100, 1000 per second.

The recording paper I have used is Du Pont Linowrit 7, 3⅝ in wide, supplied in rolls 100 ft long. The image can be produced either by photolysis or by the normal developing and fixing procedure using Du Pont liquid developer DXL148. In photolysis one makes the record, cuts off the length of paper, and exposes it emulsion side up under an ordinary fluorescent desk lamp for about two minutes. The image appears as a blue trace on a pink background. Unfortunately the image is not permanent in ordinary light and will fade out after several hours' exposure. The image can, however, be kept indefinitely in the dark and can be studied repeatedly so long as the aggregate period of exposure to daylight or incandescent light is not too long. The photolytic method is ideal for a "quick look" or for those experiments not requiring a permanent record. If the image is to be brought out by photolysis the entire process can be carried out in daylight or normal room light.

When a permanent image is required all operations must be performed under an orange safelight. The image is recorded as before, developed and fixed, washed and dried. The resulting image is as permanent as any normal black and white photographic print. I have found it possible to make the record, develop, fix, and start the washing process in six minutes.

Both the photolyzed and developed records are crisp and sharp with excellent contrast. They are easily reproduced. If one wishes, the photolyzed record can be copied photographically to produce a permanent record.

Normally the paper is started and stopped using a manually operated pushbutton. For paper speeds through 4 in/sec this is entirely convenient. At the two highest paper speeds, however, there is likely to be considerable paper wastage due to the difficulty of manually controlling the start-stop pushbutton with adequate precision. To avoid this difficulty a second circuit is used, which includes a timer which can be preset to turn off the paper drive after any desired time interval. The sweep-starting pulse from the first timing circuit of the Beckman instrument is connected to this timer through the relay mentioned earlier (p. 12). In operation one decides by inspection on the oscilloscope the appropriate delay from the starting signal, sets the interval to be recorded on the oscillograph timer, and arms the circuit by pushing a button. On the next round of the tape, travel of the oscillograph paper will be started automatically at the appropriate delay point and stopped after the time interval preset on the timer. This device is essential at 64 in/sec paper speed and highly desirable at 16 in/sec.

The input to the oscillograph is taken from the amplified signal connection on the modified oscilloscope. Since the amplitude shown on the oscilloscope and the amplitude of the signal on the oscillograph can be preset to a fixed relationship, this technique provides an easy way of controlling signal amplitudes on the oscillograph irrespective of the signal strength coming from the tape recorder. It also permits the amplification of very weak signals beyond the capacity of the amplifier in the tape recorder.

Since the writing oscillograph and its galvanometers are quite expensive, it should perhaps be emphasized that it is not an essential item since permanent records can readily be made with oscilloscope and camera, with equal precision and over an even greater range of time magnification. The merit of the writing oscillograph arises almost wholly out of the speed with which precise time-amplitude displays can be produced. A secondary advantage is that one can work directly from a tape recording at the oscillograph input. One need not first make a closed loop of the song in question. The choice of methods depends principally on the volume of data to be processed. If this is large, the oscillograph will pay its way.

The Wave Analyzer

As indicated above, the Sonagraph gives only the crudest indication of the amplitude of a given signal and will not respond at all to very weak signals. Even when sections are taken the resulting data are at best ambiguous and at worst misleading, due to the nonlinearity of the frequency-amplitude relationships.

To remedy this difficulty I have used a Hewlett-Packard, Model 300A, wave analyzer in conjunction with the oscilloscope. It was necessary to modify the instrument in two particulars. We detuned the exceedingly narrow band-pass filter to increase its value to 45 c/s and provided a relatively wide constant-response region with very sharp cutoff slopes before and beyond that region. We also modified the circuitry to permit the output signal to be displayed on the oscilloscope.

The instrument has a frequency range from essentially zero to 16,000 c/s and, by means of internal amplifiers, a very wide amplitude range. In practice only a limited portion of the amplitude range is useful since background noise on the tape recording masks signals below a certain intensity level. The limiting amplification thus depends essentially on the background noise of the recording. For good recordings one can detect harmonics with amplitudes a few tenths of a percent that of the fundamental. In all cases measurements down to one percent can readily be made.

The wave analyzer is inserted ahead of the input to the oscilloscope with a switch to permit a heterodyne output signal (20 kc/s) to be displayed on the oscilloscope. The amplitude of the signal is proportional to the amplitude of that component of the input signal found within the selected frequency band. In practice the unfiltered song is scanned using the delay counter until the signal to be analyzed appears on the grid. The wave analyzer is then switched into the circuit and the frequency dial on the analyzer rotated until maximum amplitude of the filtered signal is obtained. This establishes the frequency of the signal and its *relative* amplitude. In measuring a series of harmonics one adjusts the calibrated amplifier in the wave analyzer to obtain a sufficiently large signal on the oscilloscope grid. The relative amplitude is then the product of the signal voltage on the oscilloscope and the amplifier settings on the wave analyzer.

The wave analyzer as modified has a response band-width of 45 c/s. The effective value of the filter can be increased or decreased by appropriate changes in the speed

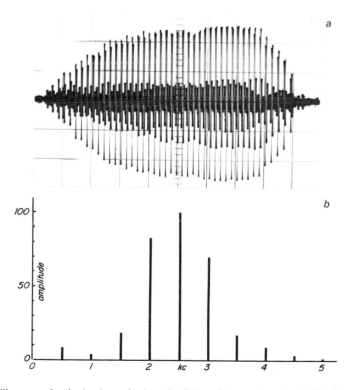

FIGURE 5. *a*, Oscillogram of a single phrase in the call of the red-breasted nuthatch. Horizontal scale 10 msec per division. *b*, Harmonic spectrum.

of the tape recorder. For example, with a tape recorded at 15 in/sec and played at $3\frac{3}{4}$ in/sec, the effective response band-width becomes 180 c/s with respect to the original frequencies.

Figure 5 shows the harmonic spectrum for the song of a red-breasted nuthatch determined with oscilloscope and wave analyzer.

High and Low Pass Filters

There are a number of situations in bird song analysis for which a pair of sharply cutting high and low pass filters are most useful. If, for example, one wishes to isolate single harmonics, or if one wishes to separate two harmonically unrelated voices in a song, such filters provide an elegant method for doing so. Furthermore, since bird song recordings invariably contain more or less background noise, adjusting the filters to include only the frequencies comprising the song itself gives much cleaner pictures on the oscilloscope or oscillograph than can be obtained with the unfiltered signal.

The two filters involve coupling a number of calibrated variable inductances and capacitances to produce the desired result. Figure 6 is a block diagram showing the arrangement of the filter components (and includes the small high pass filter mentioned on page 12); figure 7 shows their cut-off characteristics equivalent roundly to 500 db per octave. Values for the circuit elements are given in appendix 2. I have used a computer-calculated table to derive switch settings at 50-cycle frequency intervals from 200 to 10,000 c/s. Figure 8 shows a typical separation of two overlapping notes from the song of a Lapland longspur.

Of course, recordings can be made of the filtered songs by channeling the original recording through the filters and through the oscilloscope amplifier (to compensate for filter attenuation or weak signals) into a second recorder. For two-voiced songs, q.v., it is interesting to hear the individual components as well as the combination.

The Period Counter

As has been indicated earlier, frequency determination through use of electrical band-pass filters has inherent limitations in the sense that frequency measurement is essentially a counting process; hence the longer the period during which the count is made the more precisely the frequency can be measured, and vice versa. The mathematics of band-pass filtration is quite complex, but in very general terms the time delay associated with a given band-pass is the reciprocal of the width of the passed band, and any modulation either of amplitude or frequency within this interval is lost through the averaging process.

Thus for the 45 c/s filter in the Sonagraph (and in the Hewlett-Packard wave analyzer) the delay time is roundly 22 msec, and any signal modulation within this time interval will be "smeared" through the averaging process. The time delay of the

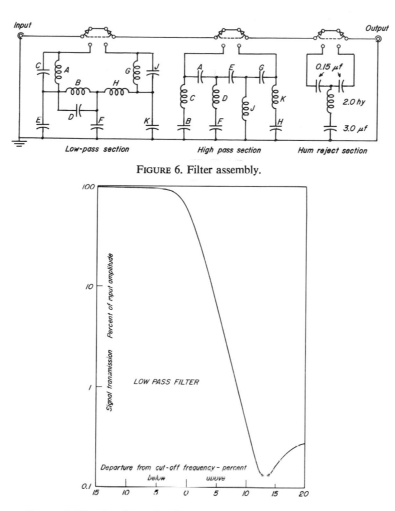

FIGURE 6. Filter assembly.

FIGURE 7. The sharply cutting filters; signal transmission as a function
of departure from cut-off frequency.

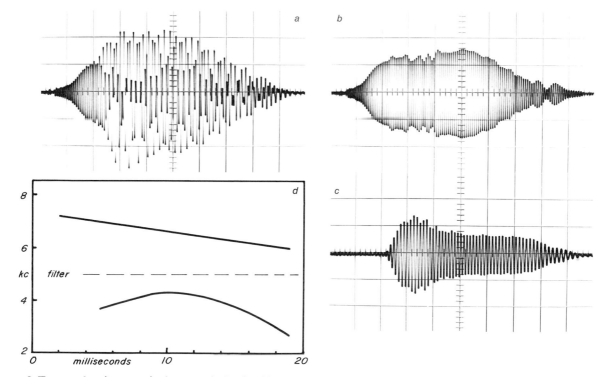

FIGURE 8. Two overlapping notes in the song of a Lapland longspur: *a*, unfiltered phrase; *b*, high note; *c*, low note; *d*, frequencies kc/s.

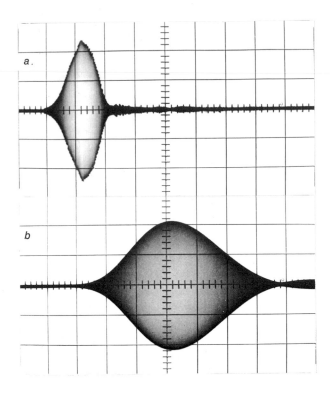

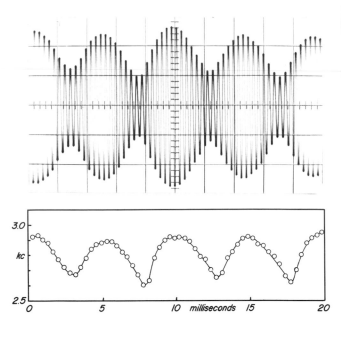

FIGURE 9. The first introductory note in the song of a grass-hopper sparrow: *a*, as shown by the oscilloscope; *b*, after passing through the Hewlett-Packard wave analyzer set at 8 kc/s (the measured frequency) and 45 c/s band-pass. The starting times are identical; the horizontal scale is 5 msec per division.

FIGURE 10. A 20 msec fragment from a phrase in the song of a Bewick's wren. Note both frequency and amplitude modulation.

FIGURE 11. One of a series of terminal phrases from the song of a song sparrow. Note the rapid glissandi.

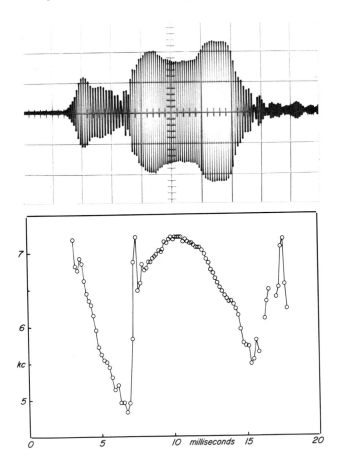

300-c/s filter is 3.3 msec, so that modulations over short time intervals can be more readily recognized; there is, however, a corresponding loss in precision on the frequency scale. Hence the use of band-pass filters invariably requires a compromise and for very short notes or for very rapid amplitude or frequency modulations the compromise may be a poor one.

Figure 9 shows first the unfiltered envelope of the first short introductory note of a grasshopper sparrow, and immediately beneath is the envelope produced by the Hewlett-Packard wave analyzer set at the frequency at which the note is sung. The time delay and envelope distortion due to the filter are readily apparent.

A way out of this dilemma is to use a period counter with the oscilloscope, in place of a band-pass filter. The instrument I have adopted is a Hewlett-Packard Model 5532A counter. This instrument, equipped with a 1-megacycle oscillator, can make single period counts to plus or minus 1 μ sec. Since bird songs rarely contain frequencies higher than 10,000 c/s, we can count on a precision of plus or minus one percent or better for the measurement of a single period.

In practice the period counter is used in conjunction with the timer-oscilloscope assembly. The input to the counter is taken from the amplified oscilloscope output. The pulse which starts the sweep circuit of the oscilloscope triggers a gating circuit which arms the start circuit of the period counter for approximately 100 msec. The first positive crossing of zero voltage level after arming starts the counter, which then measures the time interval to the next positive crossing; hence the period for that particular sine wave. By moving the signal along through appropriately small increments of the first timing circuit of the Beckman, short notes can be scanned period by period. For longer notes, particularly those whose frequency is relatively constant, the period counter can be set to average 10 or 100 periods for greater precision.

Where higher harmonics are present at substantial intensity the method fails, unless the particular harmonic is first isolated through use of the high and low pass filters, which can frequently be done.

Figure 10 shows the reciprocals of successive periods determined with the period counter for a very short fragment taken from the song of a Bewick's wren together with the amplitude envelope for the same note taken with the oscilloscope. In this case the bird is modulating both frequency and amplitude at the same modulating frequency. Figure 11 shows similar data for one of a series of very short terminal notes in the song of a song sparrow. Note the extraordinary rapidity of the glissandi, the second covering 2 kc/s in three successive periods.

Assembly

For convenience in manipulation, all of the oscilloscopic equipment except the wave analyzer has been mounted in a conventional instrument console. Figure 12 shows the assembly, and figure 13 a schematic diagram of the signal and trigger circuits for the console proper.

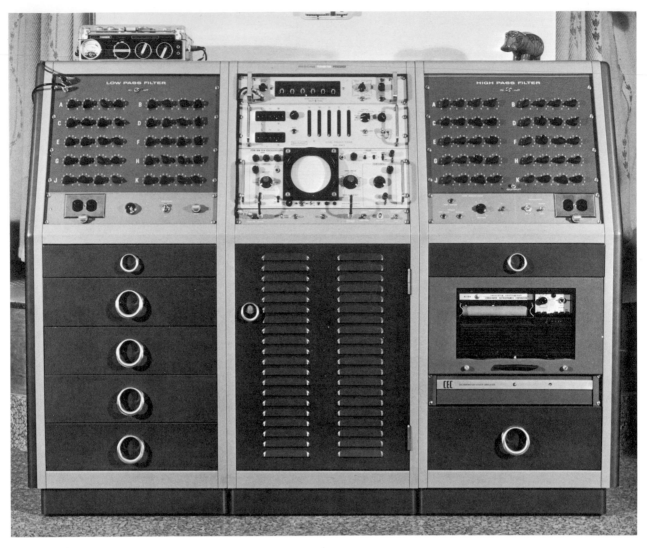

FIGURE 12. The signal analysis console.

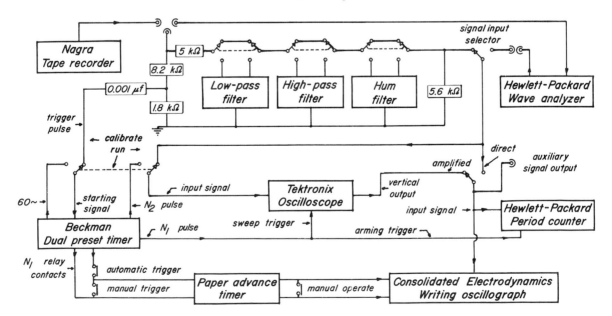

FIGURE 13. Block diagram of the signal analysis console.

The techniques used in recording bird songs are outside the scope of the present investigation. Nonetheless it seems appropriate to include a brief description here, to indicate the limitations and potential errors inherent in current procedures. Virtually all workers employ a parabolic reflector, 2–3 ft in diameter, with a focal length of 8–12 in, having a dynamic microphone mounted at its focus. A portable tape recorder equipped with headphones completes the assembly. The parabola is "pointed" at the singing bird, the sound intensity is monitored either aurally from the headphones or visually from the recorder's VU meter and the recording taken.

The most serious error arises out of the variability in the frequency/amplitude response of the assembly. The response can be constant only when the wave length of the signal is substantially less than the diameter of the parabola. A 500-c/s signal has a wave length of about 2 ft, hence the gain of the assembly falls off rapidly as the signal frequency approaches and falls below this value. Even at frequencies well above 500 c/s there is evidence to indicate that the frequency/amplitude relationship is not constant.

A second error may be introduced if the background noise, most usually produced by wind effects, is substantial in amplitude as compared to the signal itself. Here the tape may be overloaded by the background signal, thus distorting the signal arriving from the singing bird. When the background noise is at low amplitude, its effects can be largely removed by use of the filter systems previously described, but when background amplitude is high it is best to discard the recording.

For the most part I have used as source material recordings made by others, and the apparatus used and the conditions encountered were not given. Fortunately one can easily judge quality of the recording from the display on the oscilloscope, using the 300 c/s high pass filter to eliminate background noise of low amplitude.

For the few recordings I have made and used as source material here, I have used parabolas of 2- and 3-ft diameter, a high quality dynamic microphone, and the Nagra III-B recorder.

Chapter 3 THE SYRINX

The literature on the anatomy of the vocal organs of birds is voluminous and deals in more or less detail with a vast number of species. Most of the investigations are concerned with syringeal anatomy as a taxonomic tool, and present much material which is relatively unimportant from a functional or acoustical viewpoint. Even those authors interested solely in the anatomical basis for vocalization include descriptions of parts of the syrinx of doubtful acoustical significance. Hence the reader "doing his duty" by the pertinent literature is more likely to be confused than enlightened because of the abundance of material, much of it irrelevant to the mechanics of vocalization, and because of conflicting notions as to the acoustical significance of particular anatomical details. Even so there remain large experimental gaps. For example, I have found no studies of the respiratory system as it operates during vocalization, and none to indicate how the bird manipulates its respiratory organs in making the transition from normal breathing to song.

In the following discussion of the syrinx and its associated parts I have relied principally on papers by Häcker (1900), Setterwall (1901), and Rüppell (1933), from which one can extract all of the significant anatomical structures.

Rüppell takes the syrinx of the herring gull as the basic or archetype vocal organ, in the sense that it has all of the elements essential for vocalization without the anatomical embellishments characteristic of birds higher in the evolutionary scale. I paraphrase his description here.

The larynx, in birds as in humans, is at the terminus of the respiratory system. In humans the larynx contains the vocal cords which are the source of speech and song.

In birds the larynx contributes little to vocalization and appears to be used principally to protect the respiratory system during the process of feeding or regurgitation.
It is, however, equipped with musculature which can open or close the slit-like
aperture and perhaps regulate the size of the opening. Hence one must consider the
possibility that it may indeed influence vocalization by modifying the tracheal resonances even though it does not make a direct contribution to the sound-generating
process.

The trachea of the herring gull according to Rüppell is conical (figure 14a). Its
mean length is about 190 mm (136 tracheal rings) with a circumference decreasing

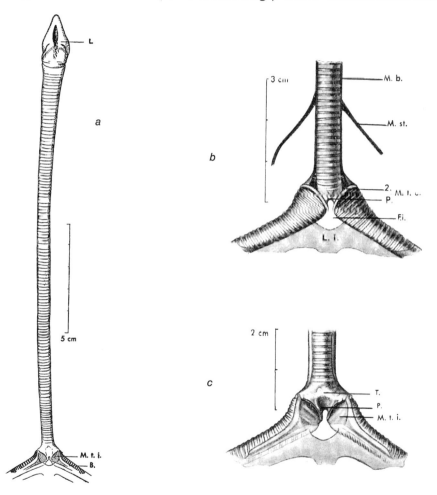

FIGURE 14. Herring gull: a, Dorsal view of trachea with larynx (L), bronchi (B), and internal membrane
(M.t.i.). The syrinx: b, ventral view; c, dorsal view. M.b., musculus broncho-trachealis; M.st., musculus
sterno-trachealis; P., pessulus; 2., second bronchial ring; M.t.e., M.t.i., membrana tympaniformis externa
and interna; T., tympanum; L.i., ligamentum interbronchiale (bronchidesmus); F.i., foramen interbronchiale.
[From Rüppell, 1933, figures 1–3.]

from 28 mm just below the larynx to 18 mm just above the syrinx. It shows a weak dorsoventral flattening, most pronounced just below the larynx. The cartilaginous tracheal rings are loosely bound together with elastic tissue. Each ring is so constructed that it can overlap its neighbor for about half its width; hence the length of the trachea can vary from a minimum of 110 mm to a maximum of 240 mm in the fully stretched condition. A pair of muscles (musculi broncho-tracheales) extend on both sides of the trachea for its entire length and are inserted in the second bronchial ring. Their contraction serves to shorten the trachea and to raise or bend apart the two bronchi. At the 16th tracheal ring from the bottom a second pair of muscles is inserted (musculi sterno-tracheales) whose caudal end is attached to the processus lateralis anterior to the breast bone.

The syrinx (figures 14b,c) is placed at the junction between trachea and bronchi and has, in the herring gull, a relatively simple structure. The first three tracheal rings are strongly ossified and fused to form the rigid tube of the tympanum. The lower edge of the first ring projects centrally at an acute angle, at whose apex the pessulus, a bony bridge, bisects the lower circumference of the trachea, creating two openings which form the points of attachment of the bronchi. Toward the lung the first pair of bronchial half rings (roughly C-shaped) are also ossified and fused to the tympanum. The second pair of half rings are cartilaginous, strongly developed, and larger in diameter than the first, particularly at their free ends. This permits movement of the ends of the second ring over the first when the axis of rotation is tangent to the outer periphery of the bronchus. The bronchial half rings (23 in number for a bronchial length of 23 mm) are bound together by elastic, transparent membranous tissue. Between the free ends of the first five bronchial rings (more widely open than the others) is suspended an exceedingly thin, glass-clear membrane (membrana tympaniformis interna) whose vibrations, under circumstances to be described, give rise to vocalization. This membrane is connected to and is in effect a modification of the membranous tissue surrounding the bronchial rings. It is roughly triangular in form, about 50 sq mm in area, and is bounded by the pessulus and the free ends of the bronchial half rings. The membrane (there are, of course, two of them, one in each bronchus) forms in effect a thin "window" in the much thicker interannular membrane surrounding the bronchus.

The two bronchi fork out from the trachea at an angle of about 100°. They are tied together by a wide band of tissue, the bronchidesmus, whose point of attachment is just below the tympaniform membrane. It will be recalled that the only muscles attached to the syrinx are the musculi broncho-tracheales which insert in the second bronchial half ring. Presumably the application or relaxation of tension in these muscles (against the restraining force of the bronchidesmus) can rotate the second bronchial half ring about an axis tangent to its outer periphery, thus modifying the longitudinal tension in the tympaniform membranes.

The syrinx is located in the pleural cavity and is closely surrounded by the inter-clavicular air sac (saccus clavicularis) which in turn communicates with the remaining air cavities. This arrangement permits pressure to be applied external to the bronchi (and tympanic membranes) which as we shall now see is vital to the sound-producing process.

It was Hérissant (1753, p. 293) who first showed the essential role played by the clavicular sac in vocalization. He found that

> the voice of the bird ceases as soon as one pierces the skin between the forked bones so that the air pressure which counterbalances the pressure within the mouthpiece [the bronchial passages] is lost. With closure of the opening the voice is heard again. [Brackets are mine.]

Evidently birds cannot sing without the application of air pressure external to the bronchi.

Rüppell (pp. 451–452) confirmed Hérissant's findings. He mounted a freshly dissected herring gull syrinx in a chamber so arranged that the chamber pressure (external to the syrinx) could be varied while at the same time blowing air through the bronchi. He reports the results as follows:

> The experiment showed that when blowing air through the bronchi in the direction of the trachea, while at the same time maintaining superatmospheric pressure in the glass chamber, the drum membranes (membranae tympaniformes internae) went into a strong oscillation and produced a loud sound, which ceased as soon as the pressure in the glass chamber was reduced to the normal atmospheric pressure (1 atm.); one could observe visually that with continued blowing through the bronchi [with atmospheric pressure in the chamber] the drum membranes bowed outward strongly, but without sound production. [Brackets are mine.]

Rüppell confirmed these observations using the syringes of other birds "which departed not too significantly from the normal type." He restricted himself to large or medium-large birds, finding it too difficult to work with the vocal organs of smaller species.

For the smaller birds and particularly the songbirds (the Oscines) I rely on the descriptions given by Häcker and Setterwall. The syringeal skeletons of the European blackbird and of the magpie, for example, differ only in detail from that of the herring gull (figures 15 and 16). There is, as before the tympanum (produced by the fusion of the last four tracheal rings), the pessulus, the first three bronchial half rings (highly differentiated as in the herring gull), and the relatively unmodified postsyringeal bronchial half rings.

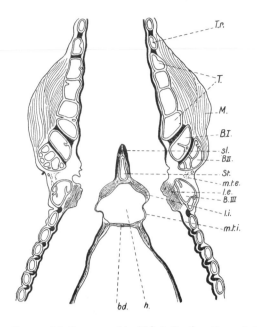

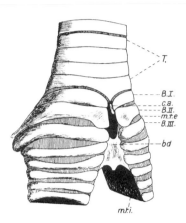

FIGURE 15. European blackbird. Section through the syrinx. T.r., tracheal ring; T., tympanum; M., musculature; sl., membrana semilunaris; B.I.–B.III, first to third bronchial half-rings; St., pessulus; m.t.e., m.t.i., membrana tympaniformis externa and interna; l.e., l.i., labium externum and internum; bd., bronchidesmus; h., space opening ventrally, section of the forward thoracic air sac. [From Häcker, 1900, figure 2.]

FIGURE 16. Magpie. Syringeal skeleton.   c.a. cartilago arytenoide. Other abbreviations as in figure 15. (The ligament connecting the lower edge of the bronchidesmus with the ventral side of the esophagus has been cut away.) [From Häcker, 1900, figure 3.]

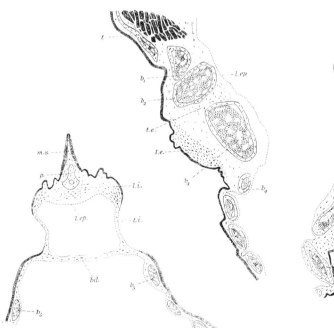

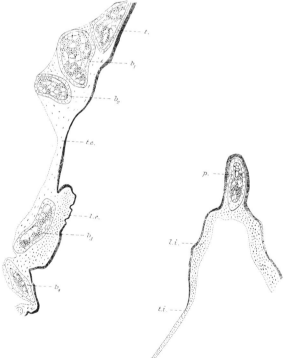

FIGURE 17. Lesser whitethroat. Frontal section through the midpoint of the right half of the syrinx. t, tympanum; b_1–b_6, bronchial half rings; p., pessulus; t.e., t.i., membrana tympaniformis externa and interna; l.e., l.i., labium externum and internum; m.s., membrana semilunaris; bd., bronchidesmus; l.ep., epithelium of the interclavicular air sac, which surrounds the syrinx. [From Setterwall, plate III:15.]

FIGURE 18. Bullfinch. Frontal section through the midpoint of the left half of the syrinx. See Figure 17 for abbreviations. [From Setterwell, plate IV:19.]

In the nonskeletal parts of the songbird syrinx differences begin to emerge. There is, for example, the cartilago tensor (Setterwall), cartilago arytenoide, or "Stellknorpel" (Häcker). This is a small cartilage which Setterwall (and others) considers as having been, before ossification, a part of the second bronchial half ring, and which in adult birds has assumed an identity of its own. Its function is obscure, but it appears to be imbedded in the upper part of the internal tympaniform membrane and may serve, in association with the syringeal musculature, to control its tension.

There is also the so-called labium externum, a pillow-like growth on the inner wall of the third bronchial half ring, placed approximately opposite to the internal tympaniform membrane. There is also the membrana tympaniformis externa filling the area created by the spatial displacement of the midpoints of the second and third bronchial half rings. There is the membrana semilunaris, a crescent-shaped extension of the membranous covering of the pessulus. Finally, there is the labium internum, not much more than a thickening of the membrana tympaniformis interna as it approaches the pessulus and the membrana semilunaris.

It should, perhaps, be pointed out here that the invariable features of the songbird syrinx comprise only the membrana tympaniformis interna and the labia externa and perhaps the cartilago tensor. The membrana semilunaris is absent as often as it is present and varies considerably in the degree of its development and its penetration into the tracheal lumen. The membrana tympaniformis externa varies greatly in area and thickness, and for both these syringeal elements there is no correlation between the evolutionary development of the particular species or the virtuosity of its song. We reproduce here two of Setterwall's beautiful engravings of syringeal cross-sections of the lesser whitethroat (figure 17) and the bullfinch (figure 18), the former with a thick external membrane of small area, the latter with a membrane which is much thinner and more extensive. In both cases it will be noted that the labium internum is scarcely sufficiently differentiated from its neighboring membranes (membrana semilunaris and membrana tympaniformis interna) to warrant giving it a separate designation.

There has been much discussion—and much disagreement— as to the significance of these syringeal elements in the vocal process itself. Savart (1826), for example, assigned great importance to the membrana semilunaris and thought he could correlate its size with the vocal abilities of the various Oscine species. Others have felt that the two membranes, viz., membrana tympaniformis interna and externa, were of critical importance, acting together like the double reed of an oboe. It seems fruitless to assemble here the various hypotheses which have been put forward. Setterwall has examined the functional possibilities thoroughly and, in my view at least, conclusively, and I can do no better than to repeat his findings here.

First as to the membrana semilunaris, Setterwall (p. 41) makes the point that the membrane is quite thick, too thick in fact to support the notion that it can vibrate at the frequencies encountered in bird song. Secondly there appears to be no muscula-ture which could, directly or indirectly, affect the tension in the membrane, hence no means for changing pitch. Finally the membrane may be small in birds with con-siderable vocal virtuosity (it is, for example, missing entirely in larks).

Miskimen (1951) has shown experimentally that removal of the membrana semi-lunaris from the syrinx of a starling made no difference in the sounds produced by blowing air through the bronchi. She also demonstrated (with anesthetized house sparrows) that sound was produced only during exhalation. If the membrana semi-lunaris were the sound-producing member, one would expect vocalization during both inhalation and exhalation.

As to the membrana tympaniformis externa, it is as noted above quite variable in thickness and area. Only in a few cases, such as the bullfinch, is the membrane thin enough to be thought of as a vibrating member, and even here the membrane (Setter-wall, p. 41) carries a muscle inserted in its lateral surface which would surely inter-fere with its performance as an oscillator.

We are left then with the membrana tympaniformis interna and the labia externa as the major anatomical elements in the production of song. The internal membrane appears without question to be the primary vibrating element. It is universally present in song birds and in the overriding majority of other species. It is extensive in area (50 sq mm in the herring gull) and exceedingly thin (Setterwall, p. 34, gives its thickness for a tree pipit as 6–7 μ). The syringeal musculature is ideally arranged to vary its tension in several directions, and finally Rüppell's (p. 451) visual observations in his glass chamber indicate it to be the sole vibrating member.

The role of the labia externa is somewhat more difficult to determine. Its position in the syrinx is directly opposite the internal membrane; hence when the latter is pushed over against it by pressure in the interclavicular sac we would seem to gain the slit-like opening essential for easy and efficient sound production. Furthermore Setterwall (pp. 40–41) points to the existence of musculature in the external membrane which he believes may operate to control the position of the labium externum with respect to the vibrating internal membrane and hence the amplitude of the sound. Of course other elements of the syringeal musculature may serve the same purpose.

We turn now to the syringeal musculature and here I paraphrase Häcker's (pp. 9–13) discussion. Earlier investigators, particularly Johannes Müller (1845), Garrod (1876), and Fürbringer (1888), have shown that such orders as Passeriformes can be arranged in a series in accordance with the complexity of the syringeal musculature. Within the Passeriformes the Clamatores are at one end of the scale and the true song birds, the Oscines, at the other.

The simplest muscular arrangement is characteristic not only of the Clamatores but of many other bird families including the cuckoos, woodpeckers, shorebirds, etc. The arrangement is that described by Rüppell for the herring gull. There is a ribbon-like muscle running down each side of the trachea and inserted at the midpoint of the second (Rüppell), third (Häcker) bronchial half ring. These are called the musculi broncho-tracheales (Rüppell), or tracheo-bronchiales (Häcker). As noted earlier (see p. 24), they may control longitudinal tension in the internal membranes by rotating the third half ring about an axis tangent to its periphery.

Next in the process of muscular development is a longitudinal splitting of the musculi broncho-tracheales into one or more ventral and dorsal pairs in which case their insertion passes from the midpoint to the two ends of the bronchial half rings. The white-crowned manakin, one of the Clamatores, (Häcker, figure 6) is typical of this arrangement.

There can then arise a division of these muscles into sections lying one behind the other, and finally as we approach the musculature of the true songbird there is a further splitting into surface and deeper layers for a considerable proliferation of muscle pairs.

To give some idea of the ultimate in muscular proliferation, I reproduce Häcker's illustration of the arrangement of the syringeal muscles for the carrion crow as figure 19. The syrinx has associated with it seven pairs of muscles, arising out of the splitting and separation of an original pair of musculi tracheo-broncheales. Of these the first is inserted on the ventral end of the second bronchial half ring and on the cartilago tensor ("Stellknorpel"), the second on the ventral end of the third bronchial half ring, the third on the dorsal end of the second half ring, the fourth on

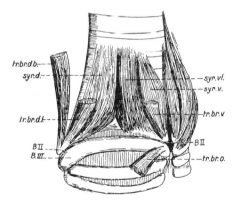

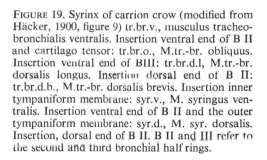

FIGURE 19. Syrinx of carrion crow (modified from Häcker, 1900, figure 9) tr.br.v., musculus tracheo-bronchialis ventralis. Insertion ventral end of B II and cartilago tensor: tr.br.o., M.tr.-br. obliquus. Insertion ventral end of BIII: tr.br.d.l, M.tr.-br. dorsalis longus. Insertion dorsal end of B II: tr.br.d.b., M.tr.-br. dorsalis brevis. Insertion inner tympaniform membrane: syr.v., M. syringus ventralis. Insertion ventral end of B II and the outer tympaniform membrane: syr.d., M. syr. dorsalis. Insertion, dorsal end of B II. B II and III refer to the second and third bronchial half rings.

the internal tympaniform membrane. Then there are (again on each side of the syrinx) three deeply placed musculi syringei; these are inserted, respectively, on the ventral end of the second bronchial half ring, on its median outer surface, and on the external tympaniform membrane.

This rather complex muscular equipment, common to most if not all true song-birds, presents the possibility of stretching the internal tympaniform membrane in almost any direction, and also of modifying the position, possibly even the shape, of the external labium.

There are also acoustical considerations which must be taken into account in assigning song-producing functions to the various syringeal parts. An extraordinary characteristic of bird song is its loudness and, particularly for the Oscines, its duration. One is astonished, for example, at the extraordinary volume of sound issuing from the male house wren; perhaps the analogy of a mouse roaring like a lion would not be too far-fetched. Such a performance must imply a very high acoustical efficiency.

Imagine, for example, a membrane, such as the internal tympaniform membrane, vibrating in a tube, namely, the bronchus. Take a cross-section of the tube at the point of maximum amplitude of the vibrating membrane. To borrow electrical terminology we call the cross-sectional area traversed by the vibrating membrane the AC component, the mean area the DC component. The membrane has been induced to vibrate by air flowing through the bronchus and a pressure drop is created as the air passes through the constricted area. Now only the AC component of the flowing air converts to acoustical energy; the DC component is wasted. For highest acoustical efficiency we must then postulate a slit, not much wider than the maximum amplitude of the vibrating member. Such a situation is impossible for the membrana semilunaris, and most difficult to imagine for the external tympaniform membrane. There is, however, no difficulty at all in postulating a condition leading to high acoustical efficiency when we consider the internal tympaniform membrane, bowed inward by pressure in the clavicular sac, until it nearly touches the opposing external labium.

All this, of course, is sheer speculation, since no one has as yet been able to devise experiments with living birds which would settle conclusively the acoustical function of the various syringeal parts. The Bell Telephone Laboratories were able, some years ago, to take moving pictures of the human glottis while the subject was speaking. But when one considers the much deeper placement of the avian syrinx in the respiratory tract, the small body size, and the extreme unlikelihood of producing a cooperative attitude in the subject, I suspect that not even the Bell scientists could produce a successful in vivo experiment.

Chapter 4 A PORTFOLIO OF WHISTLED SONG

As a preamble to the experimental part of this report, I present here a portfolio of "whistled" songs, selected to give a representative sampling of this form of vocalization within the evolutionary sequence from loon to longspur. Before explaining the significance of the term "whistled" song, it seems appropriate to discuss the somewhat unsatisfactory state of the terminology which has developed for bird song.

The characterization of bird sounds as "song" is firmly rooted in tradition, and this in spite of the fact that many bird songs are neither musical nor pleasing to human ears. It is difficult, for example, to imagine "song" as fairly descriptive of the utterances of thrush or song sparrow on the one hand and of crow or duck on the other; however, no better term has been suggested. "Vocalization" is awkward, "sound" has too many other connotations, and it must be admitted that "bird song" has the merit of common usage and understanding.

When we invert the phrase "bird song" to "songbird" we encounter completely different implications. For "songbirds" have come to represent the Oscines, a suborder of the order Passeriformes, the grouping deriving primarily from the elaboration of syringeal musculature, not from the vocalizations per se. In the older literature the designation Clamatores was used for the remaining suborders of the Passeriformes, but at present the Clamatores appear to have been replaced by the suborders Eurylaimi and Tyranni.

It seems quite certain that one would attract ornithological thunderbolts were he to characterize the common loon, for example, or the pied-billed grebe, or the golden plover, as songbirds. And yet to human ears there is no real distinction between these songs and those of the tufted titmouse, the black-capped chickadee, the varied thrush, Harris' sparrow—all members in good standing of the suborder Oscines. Within the Clamatores there are also contradictions since most of the Corvidae are surely Clamatores to our human ears whereas many of the Tyrannidae are just as surely Oscines by the same test.

I have neither the ability nor the inclination to develop new nomenclature in this confusing area, but I must nonetheless make my own meaning clear, and have coined the adjective "whistled" to be used with song or call as the case may be. "Whistled" is intended to characterize a song or call which is substantially free of harmonic content, whose wave forms are almost universally pure sinusoids, and which in turn may be modulated in frequency or in amplitude or in both. On this basis the common loon, the chickadee, and the song sparrow produce "whistled" songs which differ simply in the elaboration of their modulations. The adjective has no taxonomic significance, referring only to the acoustical character of the song being described.

The term "whistled" is used because our human whistle is a very close acoustical approach to this kind of bird song. I suspect that given an accomplished whistler, and the possibility of artificially raising pitch and modulation frequency into the avian range, it would be possible to produce a reasonably good match for those "whistled" bird songs in which only one of the two acoustical sources is used.

While on the subject of terminology, it might be well to deal here with the designations to be used for portions or fragments of a song. I note in the recent literature a tendency to refer to song fragments as "syllables," which seems to be carrying anthropomorphism a bit too far. For the term "syllable" is quite clearly limited to human speech, and if it is to be used one should refer to syllables combining to form words, words to form phrases or sentences, sentences to paragraphs, and so on. Surely there is no authority for such terminology in the singing of birds and no behavioral evidence that they "speak" to each other as humans do. If we are to retain bird "song," we might as well use musical terminology for the parts of a song and so do no violence to analogy beyond the original characterization of avian vocalization as "song."

I use the word "note" to characterize a short sound whose frequency is substantially constant. A "phrase" is either a series of related notes, or a highly modulated sound of relatively long duration. A "glissando" is a slur reaching either up or down from one frequency to another. "Vibrato" or "tremolo" could have been used to characterize phrases modulated in frequency or amplitude or both, but in bird song the modulation frequency is normally so high and the swings in frequency or amplitude so great as to fall well outside the range of "vibrato" or "tremolo" in human experience. Hence I have used the admittedly more awkward designations "frequency" or "amplitude" modulation to characterize such sounds. One can also properly speak of musical intervals, viz., a half or a whole tone, a third, a sixth, or an octave to characterize differences in frequency. Since pitch discrimination in birds is not far removed from our own,[4] musical intervals have more real meaning than frequency differences which in cycles per second are misleadingly great in the ranges encountered in bird song. A difference of 250 c/s, for example, is a full octave above middle C but scarcely a half tone at 5000 c/s, the midpoint of the range of a song sparrow. The Sonagraph has a linear frequency scale; it would perhaps have been more informative had the scale been logarithmic, corresponding more precisely to pitch discrimination as it exists both for human and avian ears.

To return now to the portfolio of "whistled" song, it is presented at the risk of some redundancy, for two reasons. While many sonagrams of bird songs have appeared in ornithological papers, these have dealt with individual species or with related species, and I have seen no collection of sonagrams portraying bird song as it develops along the evolutionary sequence. As to oscillograms of bird songs, I have seen none at all. Hence there is at least novelty, if not utility, in showing oscillograms, that is, precise time-amplitude arrays, along with the corresponding time-frequency displays. The oscillograms and sonagrams (figures 20–39) are shown one above the other with a common time axis. For the great majority of the sonagrams the recordings have been played at half speed using the narrow band-pass filter, thus producing a band width of 90 c/s with respect to the true frequencies. In a few low frequency cases the recordings are played at full speed, to avoid overcompression of the frequency scale.

In selecting the songs to be displayed I have attempted to produce a random sampling among the various orders and families. The songs were taken principally from the recordings provided for Peterson's Eastern and Western Field Guides, with a few additions from recordings produced by the Federation of Ontario Naturalists. They are reproduced on one of the two records which accompany this volume. It should perhaps be added that the displays were made using a copy of the master tape from which the records were produced, since the records themselves have too much background noise to produce clean oscillograms.

Only the roughest generalizations can be extracted from the song sequence. It is clear, for example, that the songs appear to increase in elaboration as one goes from loon to longspur, but it must be noted also that the short-billed dowitcher has a song considerably more elaborate than, let us say, the Carolina chickadee, and that the tufted titmouse and cardinal, if judged by song alone, would be placed not far from loon and grebe. The frequency range embraced within the songs appears to increase with advancing evolutionary position. Loon and grebe have songs contained in an interval less than an octave, whereas wood thrush and song sparrow have ranges encompassing two full octaves. The lowest frequency is in the song of the spruce grouse, 80–90 c/s, the highest in the terminal phrase of the cowbird,

4. Chapter 9.

nearly 11,000 c/s. The blackpoll warbler sings its entire song within the range 8,500–10,500 c/s. The greatest range within a single song is found for the cowbird whose "glug" phrase has components at 700 c/s and whose "gleeee" approaches 11,000 c/s, an interval of nearly four octaves.

One can find no consistent relationship between the frequency in the song and the size of the bird. Quite large birds, the osprey or the Laysan albatross, sing at high frequencies, whereas smaller birds quite often have relatively deep voices, for example, the mourning dove, several small owls, or the low portions of the brown-headed cowbird's song.

Finally one sees in the oscillograms a wealth of detail which is missing in the sonagrams. Here perhaps is a clue to recognition among individuals of species having a relatively simple song. This should be worth exploration by the behaviorists, for amplitude modulations may be quite as important, perhaps even more important, than the frequency or pitch at which the various phrases are sung.

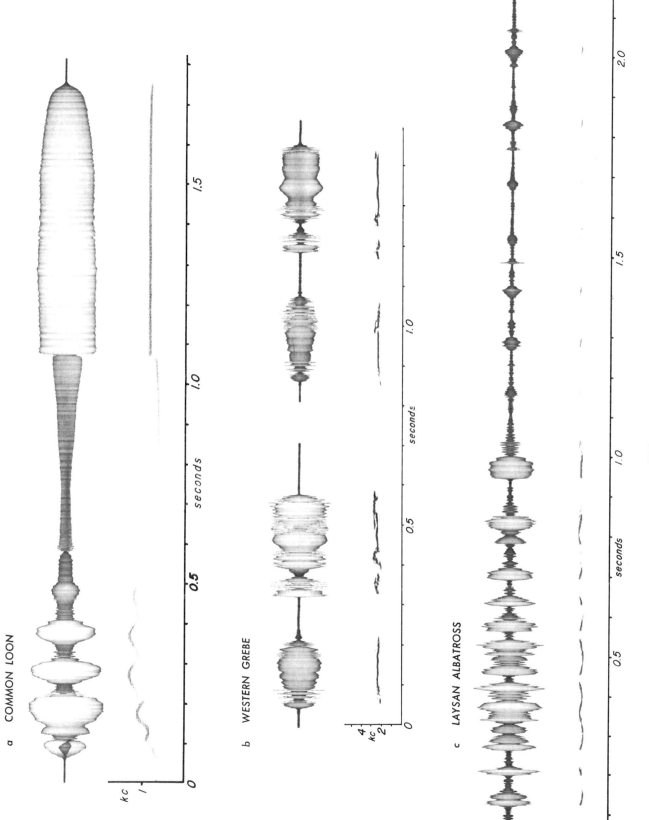

a COMMON LOON

b WESTERN GREBE

c LAYSAN ALBATROSS

FIGURE 20

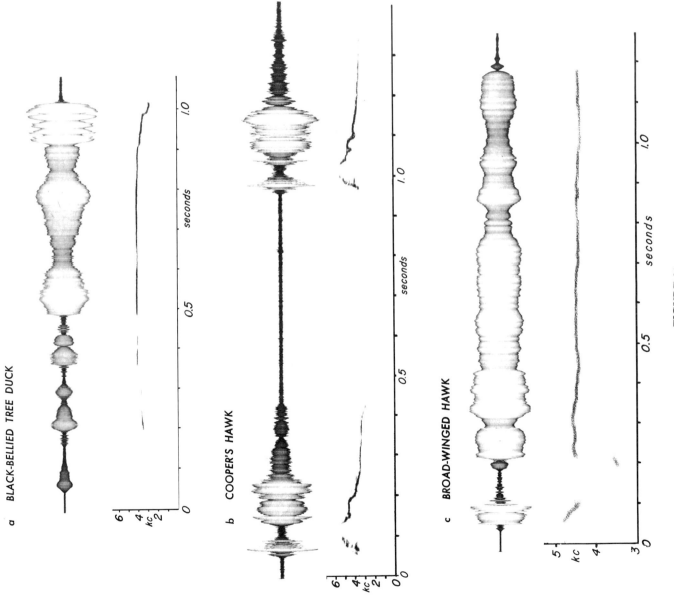

a   BLACK-BELLIED TREE DUCK

b   COOPER'S HAWK

c   BROAD-WINGED HAWK

FIGURE 21

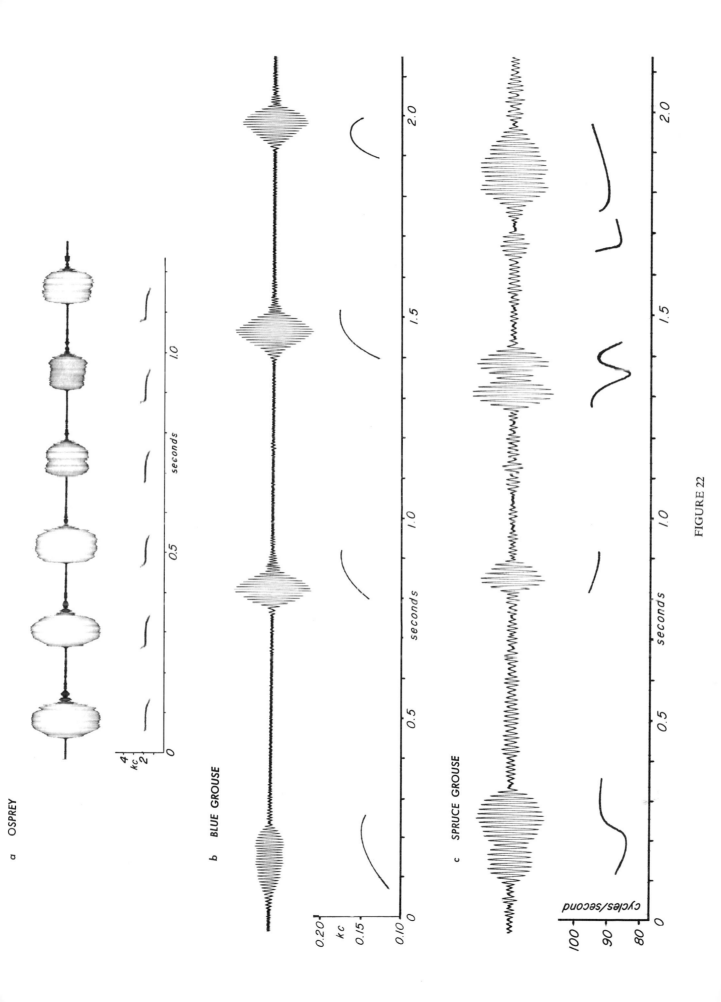

a OSPREY

b BLUE GROUSE

c SPRUCE GROUSE

FIGURE 22

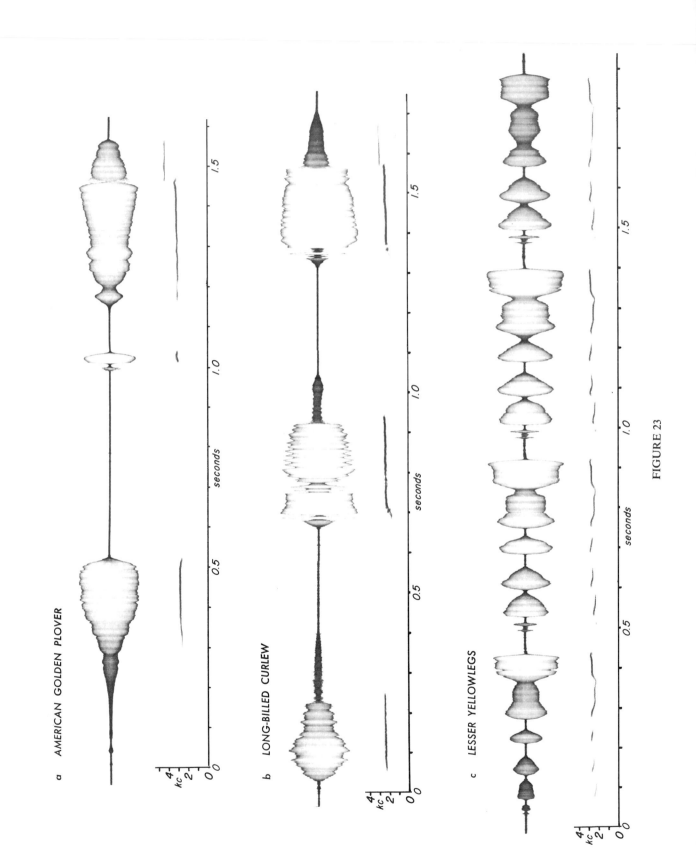

a   AMERICAN GOLDEN PLOVER

b   LONG-BILLED CURLEW

c   LESSER YELLOWLEGS

FIGURE 23

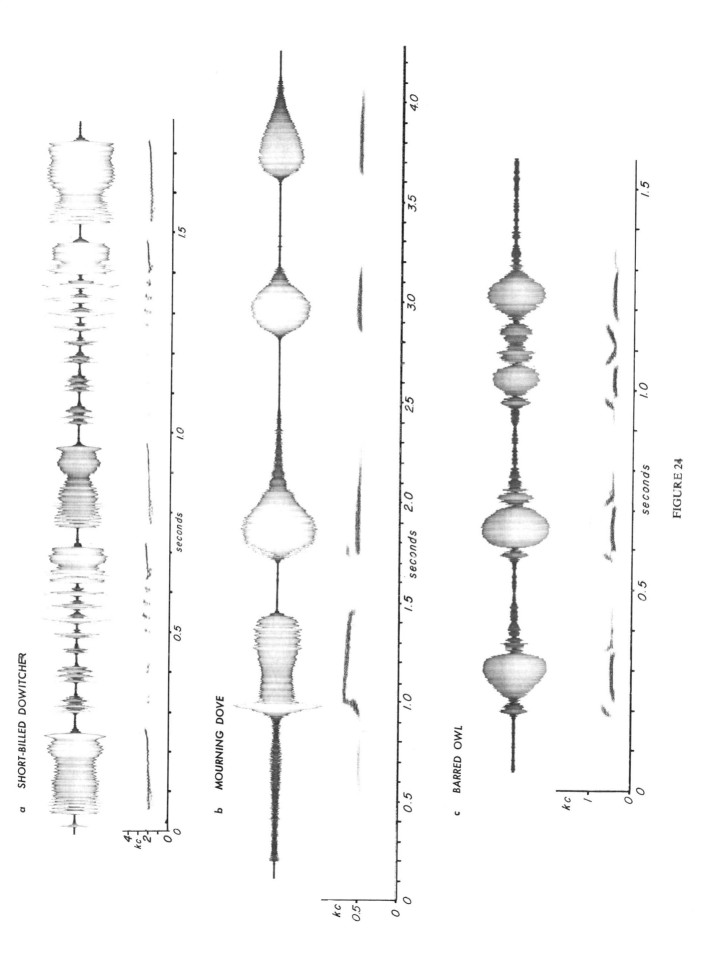

a SHORT-BILLED DOWITCHER

b MOURNING DOVE

c BARRED OWL

FIGURE 24

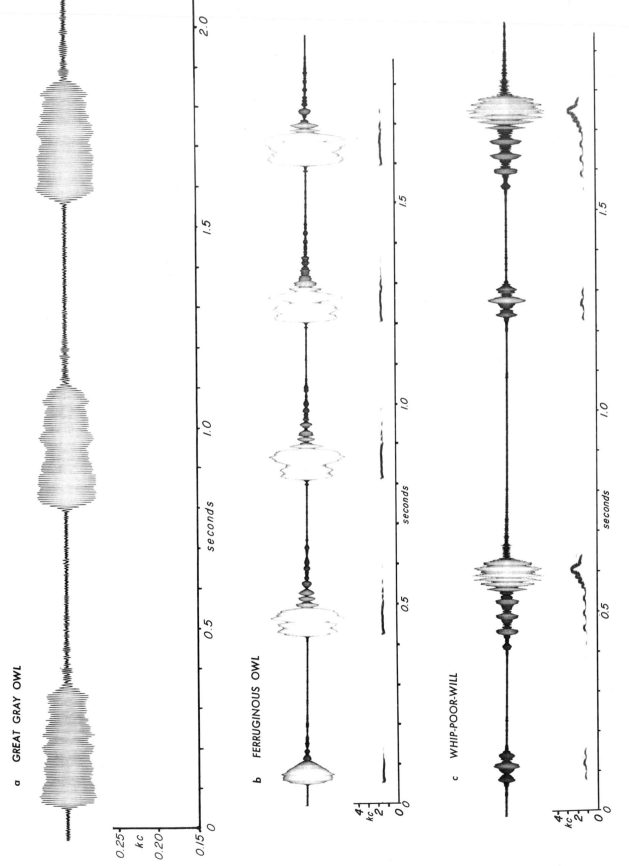

a   GREAT GRAY OWL

b   FERRUGINOUS OWL

c   WHIP-POOR-WILL

FIGURE 25

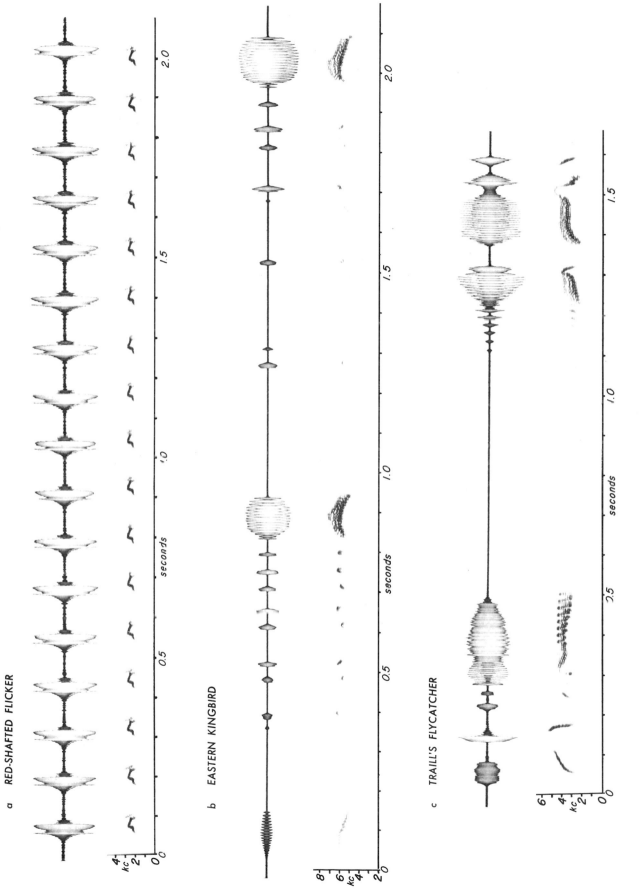

a   RED-SHAFTED FLICKER

b   EASTERN KINGBIRD

c   TRAILL'S FLYCATCHER

FIGURE 26

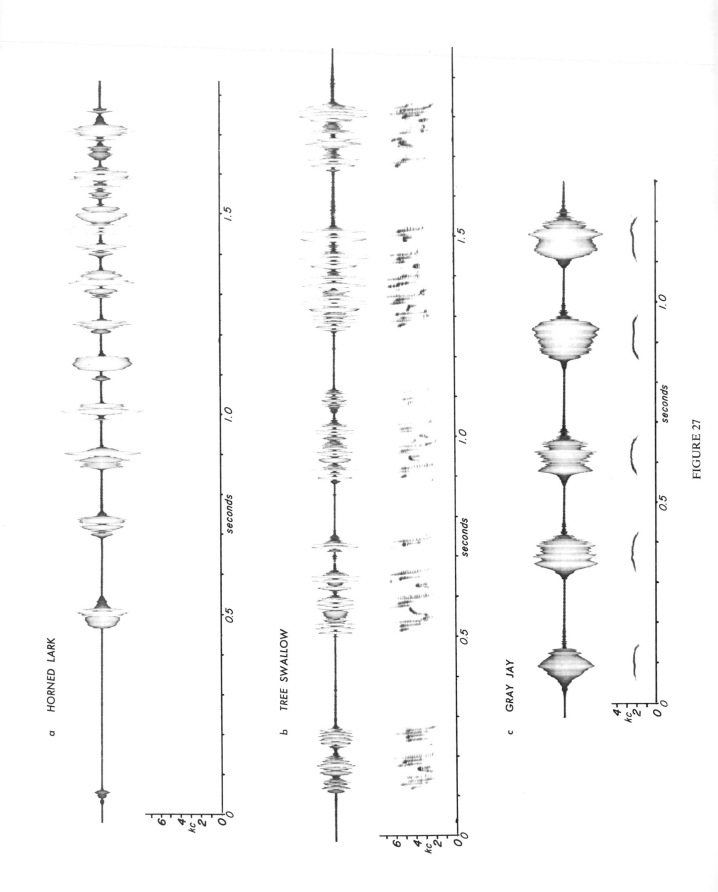

FIGURE 27

a CAROLINA CHICKADEE

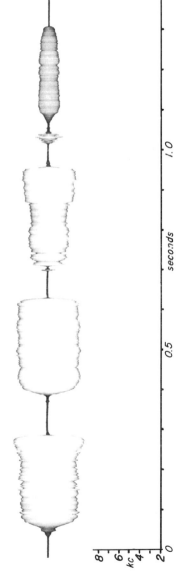

b TUFTED TITMOUSE

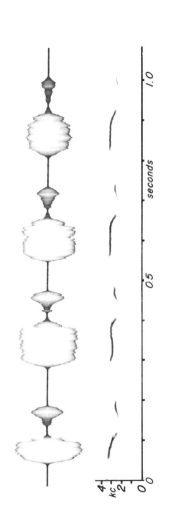

c PYGMY NUTHATCH

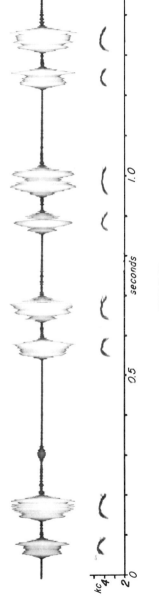

FIGURE 28

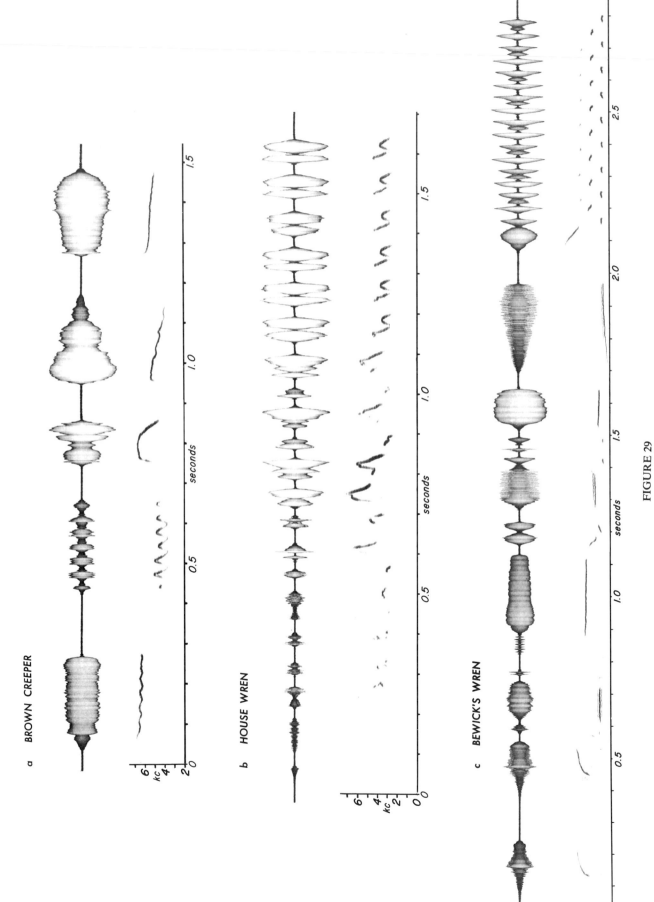

a BROWN CREEPER

b HOUSE WREN

c BEWICK'S WREN

FIGURE 29

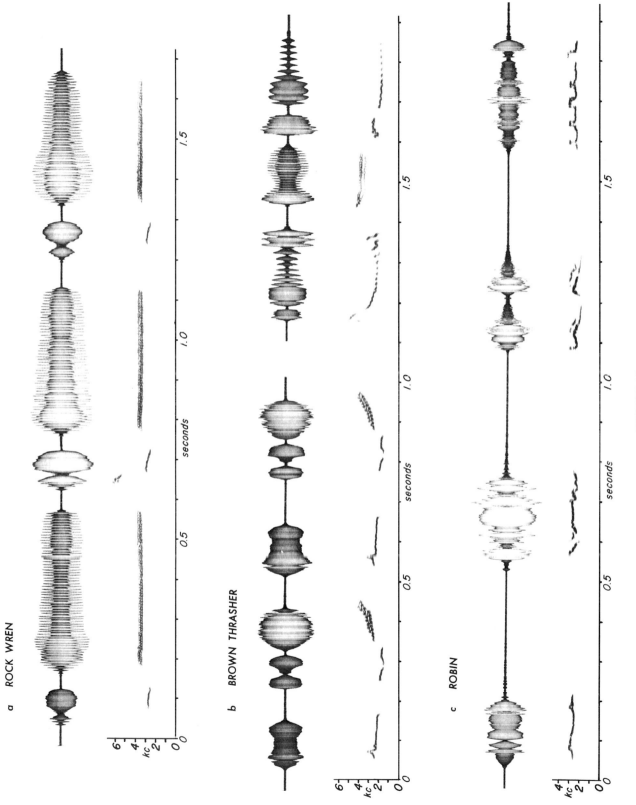

a   ROCK WREN

b   BROWN THRASHER

c   ROBIN

FIGURE 30

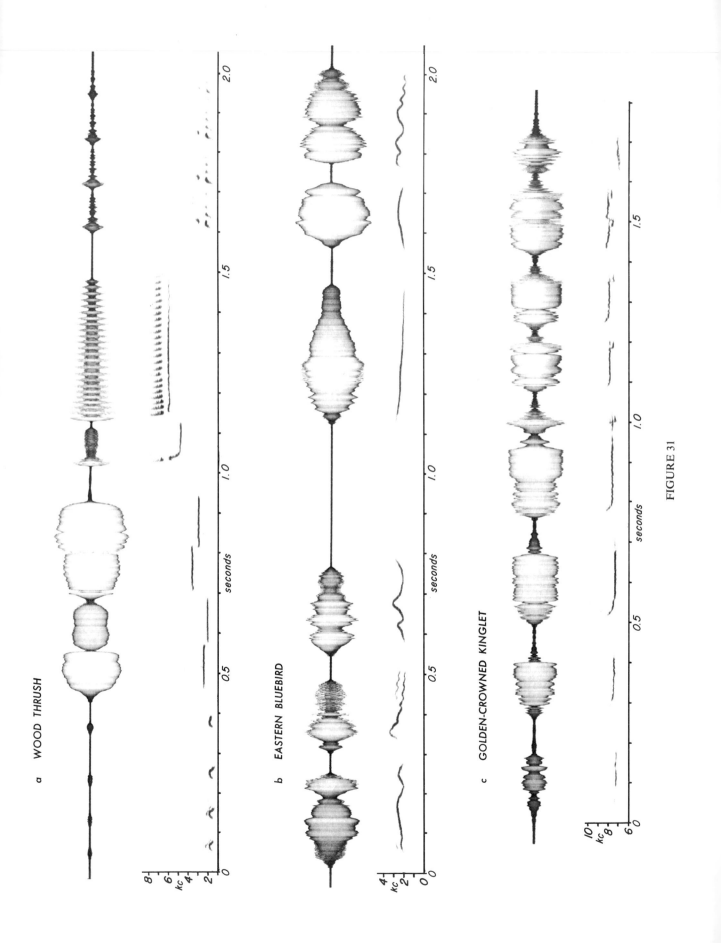

a WOOD THRUSH

b EASTERN BLUEBIRD

c GOLDEN-CROWNED KINGLET

FIGURE 31

a LOGGERHEAD SHRIKE

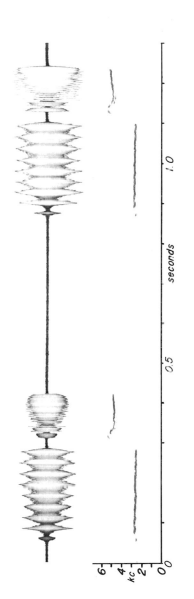

b WHITE-EYED VIREO

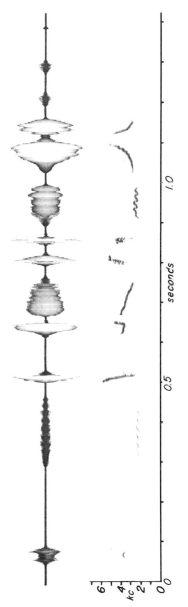

c PROTHONOTARY WARBLER

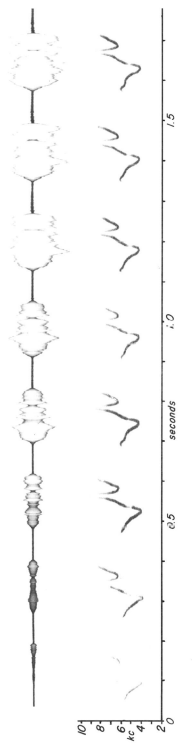

FIGURE 32

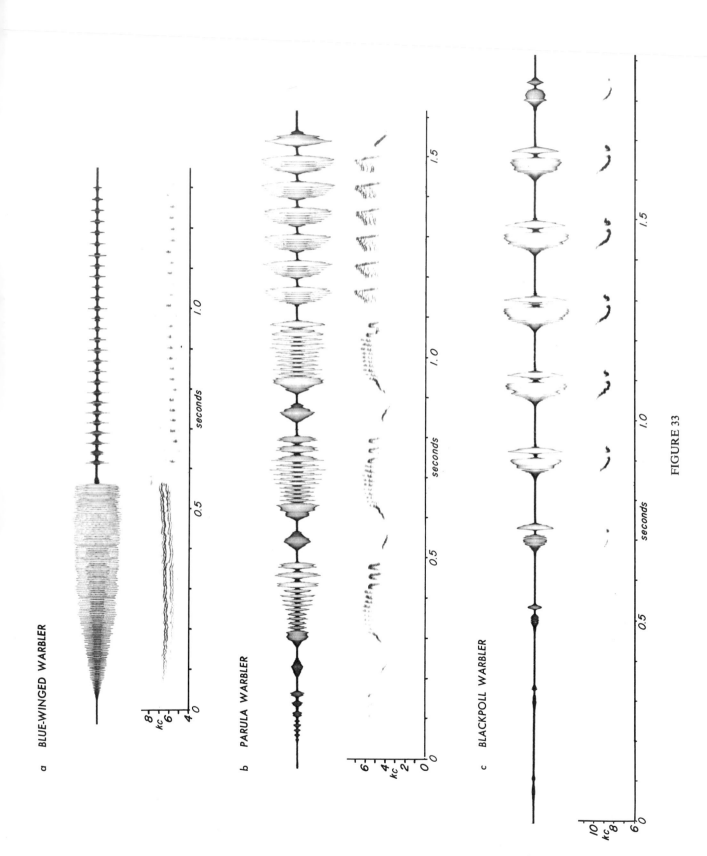

a   BLUE-WINGED WARBLER

b   PARULA WARBLER

c   BLACKPOLL WARBLER

FIGURE 33

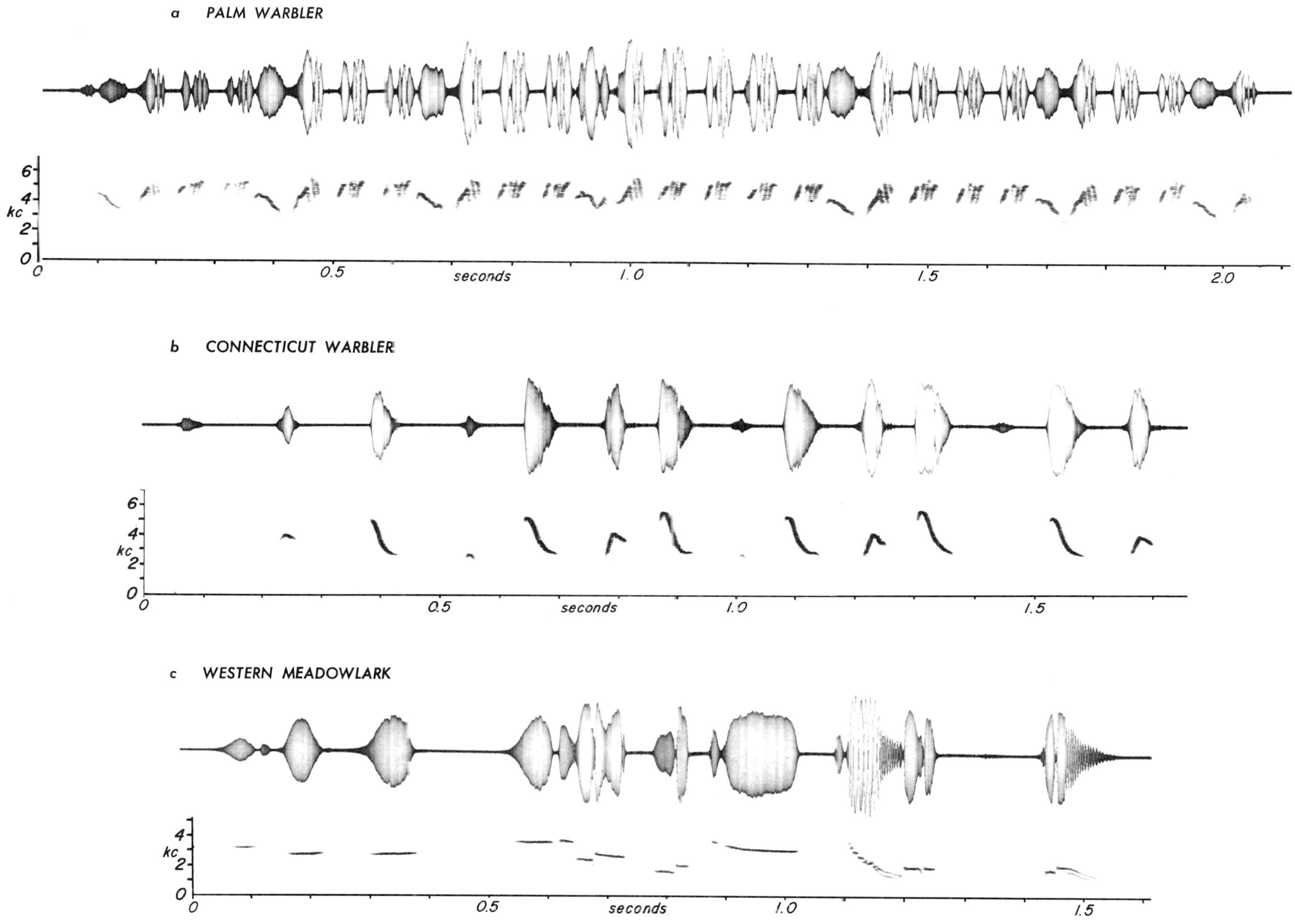

a PALM WARBLER

b CONNECTICUT WARBLER

c WESTERN MEADOWLARK

FIGURE 34

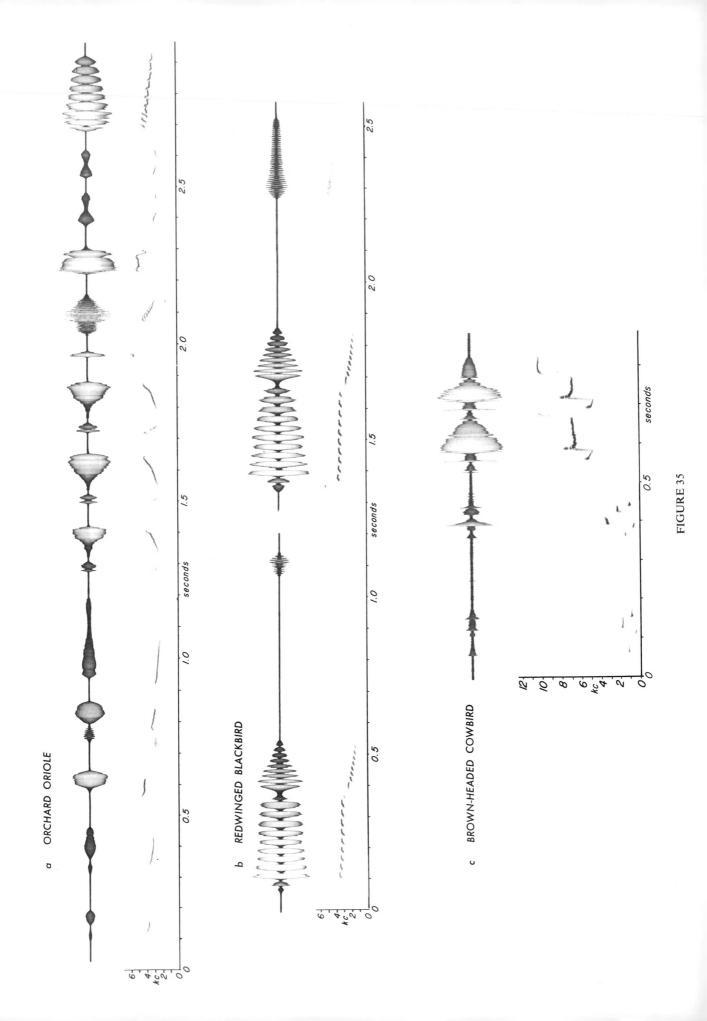

a ORCHARD ORIOLE

b REDWINGED BLACKBIRD

c BROWN-HEADED COWBIRD

FIGURE 35

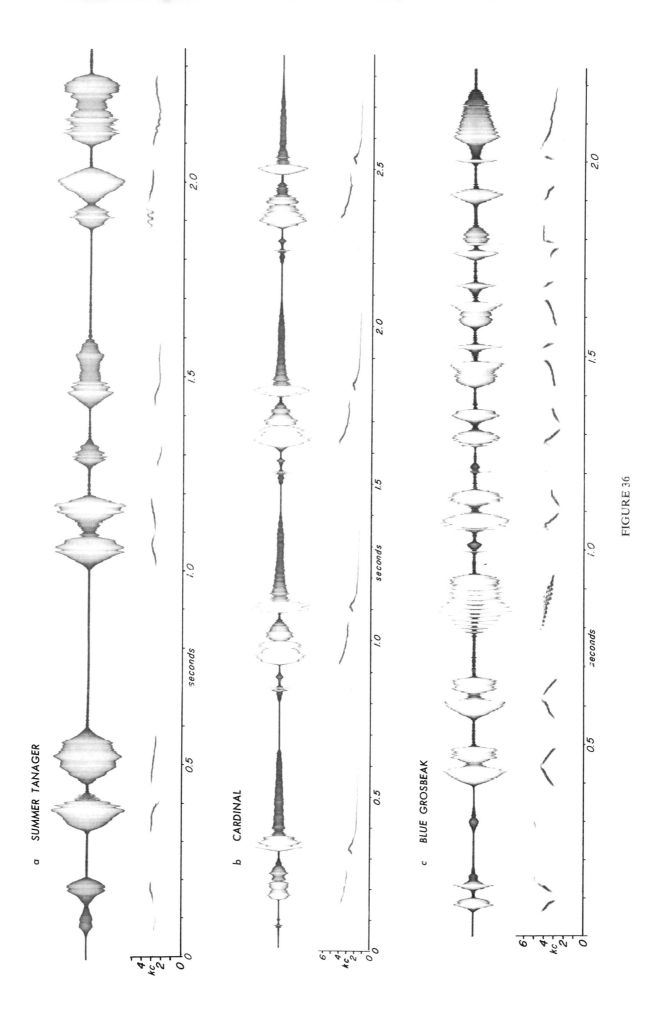

a SUMMER TANAGER

b CARDINAL

c BLUE GROSBEAK

FIGURE 36

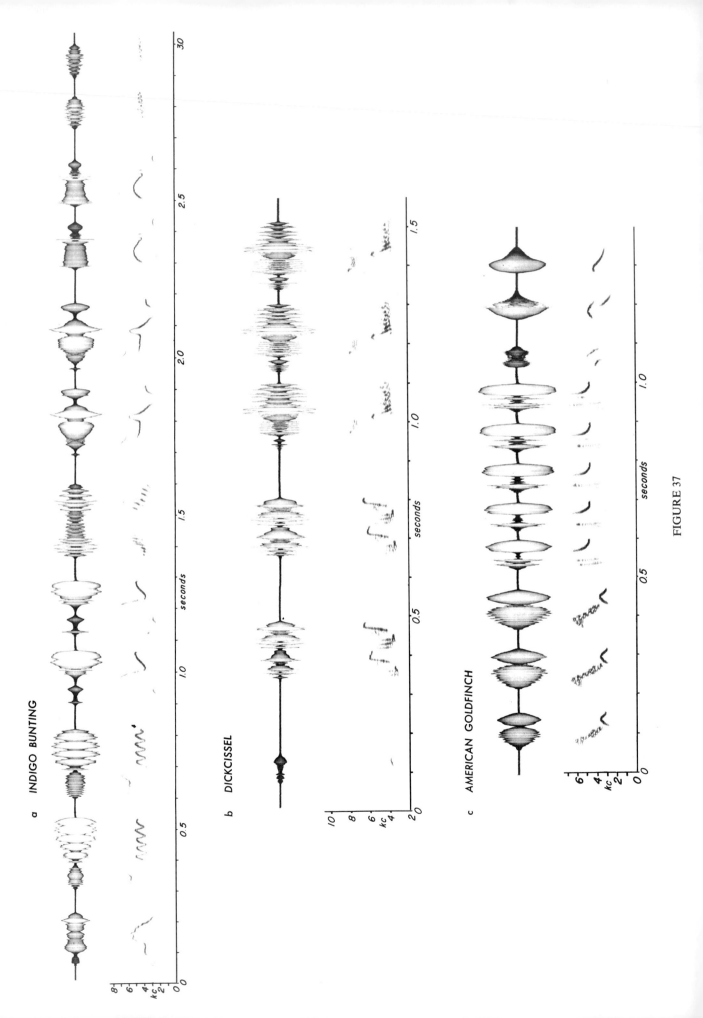

a   INDIGO BUNTING

b   DICKCISSEL

c   AMERICAN GOLDFINCH

FIGURE 37

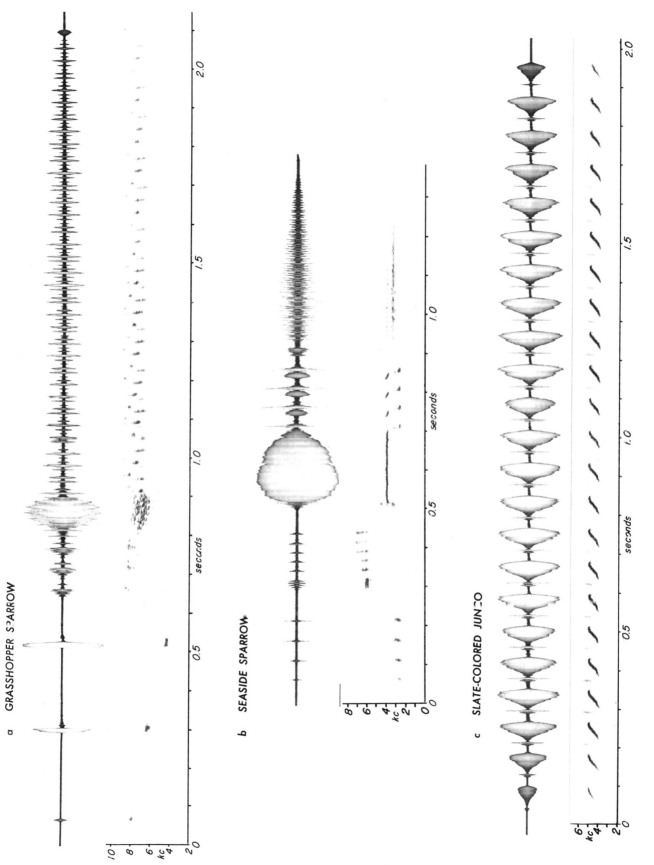

a GRASSHOPPER SPARROW

b SEASIDE SPARROW

c SLATE-COLORED JUNCO

FIGURE 38

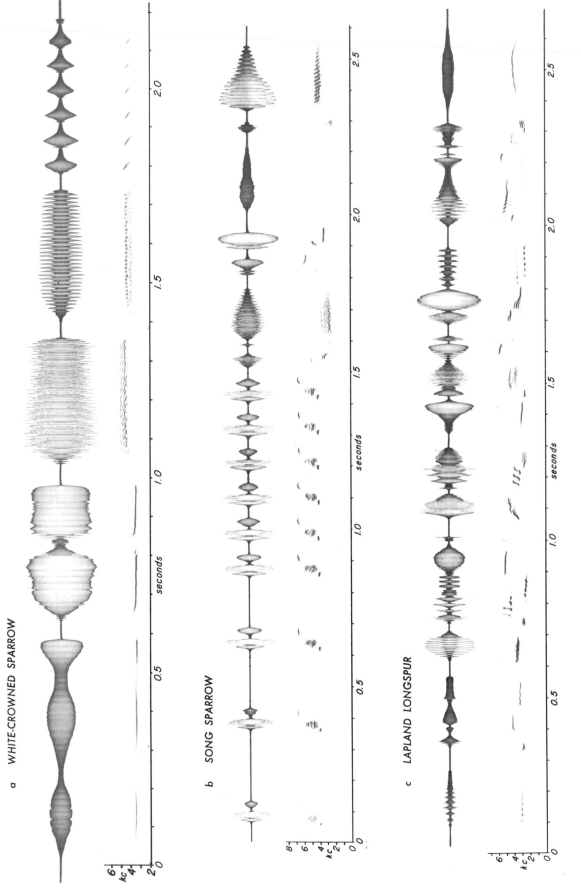

a WHITE-CROWNED SPARROW

b SONG SPARROW

c LAPLAND LONGSPUR

FIGURE 39

Chapter 5 THE TWO ACOUSTICAL SOURCES

It has been known for many years that the syrinx of the overwhelming majority of birds comprises two separate and distinct acoustical sources, one in each bronchus, each with its independent musculature and innervation. There has, however, been a reluctance on the part of earlier investigators to consider seriously the possibility that the two sources can act independently to produce in effect a double note or phrase.

Savart (1826, p. 123), for example, states that the trachea "is equipped with a double mouthpiece, an arrangement contributing much to the intensity of the sound and to its purity." He (p. 124) suggests in fact that the principle of the double mouthpiece could well be used in the construction of organ pipes and states that such an arrangement would produce sounds of greater "intensity and roundness."

Grützner (1879, p. 144) assumes that birds "must adjust their two larynges in an identical manner if two different tones are not to arise simultaneously." He suggests that in certain cases, and particularly for domesticated birds, "their loud, repulsive cries can with close attention be resolved into two nearby dissonant tones."

Häcker (1900, p. 17) accepts the Grützner postulate, stating that the generally symmetrical structure of the two sources suggests that they would deliver sounds of equal pitch and intensity; hence doubling the acoustical source serves merely to produce an increase in the loudness of the sound.

Rüppell (1933, pp. 489–495) in his long monograph discusses the question without, however, appearing to come to a firm conclusion. He considers it likely that under normal circumstances the two sources will produce identical sounds but leaves open the possibility that when they are anatomically asymmetrical, two different sounds might be produced.

The first suggestion that birds might control their two acoustical sources independently was made by Potter, Kopp, and Green (1947) in their book "Visible Speech." The last few chapters deal with possible uses for the Sonagraph outside the realm of human speech, and show among other things a number of sonagrams of bird songs. Referring to the song of a brown thrasher, they (p. 411) say ". . . and in the first part of the three notes toward the right will be found a 'double tone' sound in which two tones without harmonic relation are evident for a short interval. Presumably these must originate in separate parts of the tone-producing mechanism."

Some years later Borror and Reese (1956) showed that songs of a wood thrush contained two harmonically unrelated sounds overlapping in time. They did not, however, postulate an anatomical mechanism through which this condition could arise.

Thorpe (1961) appears willing to consider the possibility of three and perhaps four independent acoustical sources. In discussing the anatomical features which might give rise to this diversity of sound, he suggests the internal tympaniform membranes acting together as a *single* source, the external tympaniform membranes as a *second*, and the semilunar membrane as a *third*. He was unable to suggest a reasonable basis for the *fourth*.

In view of the findings of Setterwall (1901) and Miskimen (1951), it appears necessary to reject the external tympaniform membranes and the semilunar membrane as acoustical sources. As has been indicated (see pp. 27–28), the external membranes are too thick, the semilunar membrane has no directly associated musculature, and both are too variable from species to species. It is much more reasonable to suppose that if there are indeed two sources these must comprise the two internal tympaniform membranes, acting independently under the influence of their separate musculature and innervation.

The presence or absence of two independent sources is of course central to the development of an acceptable hypothesis for the acoustical processes involved in bird song; hence I have attempted to explore the question in considerable detail, for the songs of species representing most of the living groups of birds.

The technique used is as follows: A sonagram produced with the narrow band-pass filter is examined for overlapping notes which are harmonically unrelated. When such an example is found, the phrase is displayed on the oscilloscope and one easily sees the overlapping portion by noting discontinuities in the wave form. The sharply cutting filters are then adjusted to separate one note from the other and the two notes or phrases are displayed on the oscilloscope using the same time scale.

Figures 40 *a,b* show the oscillogram and the corresponding sonagram for a fragment of the song of a song sparrow. It will be seen from the sonagram that the two notes, which appear to overlap slightly, are harmonically unrelated, and from the oscillogram that there is a discontinuity in the wave form in the overlapping region.

Figures 40 *c–e* illustrate the separation of the two overlapping notes using the sharply cutting filters, together with a graph showing frequencies measured with the period counter. We see that there is indeed a substantial overlapping region (about 12 msec), proof that two separate acoustical sources must have been involved in producing the phrase.

Figures 41 and 42 show two additional examples. Figure 41 is a fragment from the introductory note of a song sparrow, with a 15 msec overlap of the two voices. Figure 42 is a phrase sung by a mockingbird in which the two voices are coextensive for the entire 300-msec phrase.

In figure 40 the time-amplitude arrays are photographs of the face of the oscilloscope; in figures 41 and 42 they were recorded on the writing oscillograph.

Examples of this sort can be found for almost every avian family. In the illustrations which follow examples are included which show the widespread occurrence of the phenomenon and the many different forms the overlapping notes or phrases may take.

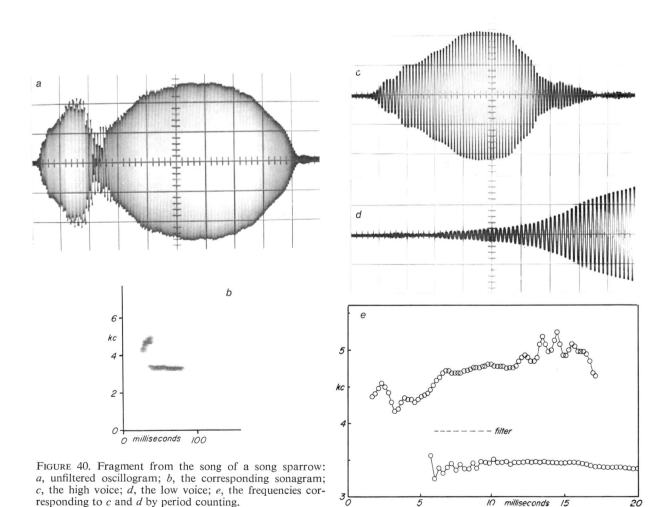

FIGURE 40. Fragment from the song of a song sparrow: *a*, unfiltered oscillogram; *b*, the corresponding sonagram; *c*, the high voice; *d*, the low voice; *e*, the frequencies corresponding to *c* and *d* by period counting.

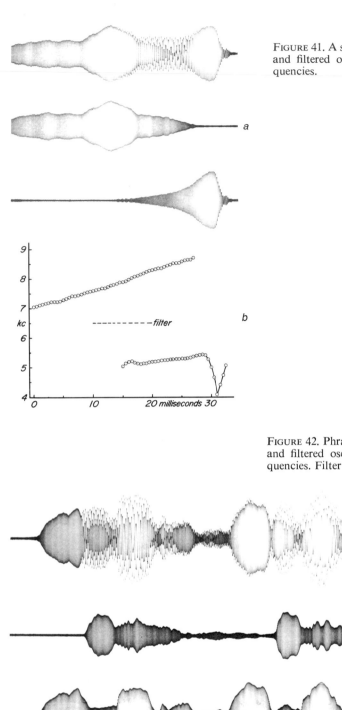

FIGURE 41. A song sparrow fragment: *a*, the unfiltered and filtered oscillograms; *b*, the corresponding frequencies.

FIGURE 42. Phrase of a mockingbird: *a*, the unfiltered and filtered oscillograms; *b*, the corresponding frequencies. Filter setting 3.2 kc/s.

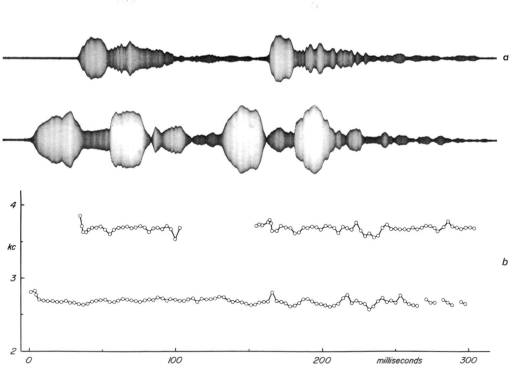

While a great many bird songs have been examined searching for this phenomenon, these have included only a minute percentage of the many thousands of singing species. The sample is, however, a reasonable one and affords sufficiently good evidence that the simultaneous use of two acoustical sources is relatively common.

I should perhaps point out that the technique described for showing the sounds from the two sources individually is possible only when they are separated sufficiently in frequency to permit insertion of the filter between them. When the frequencies of the two notes are very close, or when both are glissandi covering the same frequency range, or when each is frequency modulated to an extent producing an overlap in the side bands, the method fails. Furthermore when one sees a series of notes separated by a region of zero amplitude there is no way of being certain whether these are produced by one acoustical source or by two. These points are made to indicate that the cases shown here almost certainly represent only a small percentage of those in which two independent sources are employed.

Figures 43–72 which follow speak for themselves. In each case (except for figures 53, 54, and 73) the unfiltered oscillogram is shown at upper left and the associated time-frequency plot, which also shows the filter setting, is immediately below. At the right are the filtered oscillograms, the high voice above, the low voice below. Oscillograms and frequency plot have the same time scale and the oscillograms in each figure (with the indicated exceptions) were made at the same amplitude setting. In many cases only a fragment of the two-voiced phrase is shown, to present greater detail for the overlapping portion.

The eared grebe (figure 43) is the first bird (in an evolutionary sense) for which there is a clear showing of a pair of overlapping notes. The situation is different only in degree from the song sparrow phrase shown in figure 40.

For the American bittern (figure 44) the phrase is from the so-called "pumping" song. One sees that the two overlapping notes are coextensive in time and separated by an unusually large frequency interval; nearly two octaves.

In figure 47, greater yellowlegs, it will be seen that there is a sharp drop in amplitude for the "first voice" as the second begins. The same effect is apparent for the red-shafted flicker (figure 48), the gray-cheeked thrush (figure 58), the garden warbler, (figure 60), and the American goldfinch (figure 65). These effects may of course be voluntary on the part of the singer, but it is perhaps more likely that division of the air flow between the two bronchi and their associated vibrating members produces an involuntary drop in amplitude.

The peculiar anvil-like call of the naked-throated bellbird arises out of two successive notes exactly an octave apart which overlap slightly. Figure 49 shows only the overlapping region.

The green jay (figure 51) is a good example of rapid and asymmetrical amplitude modulation for each of the two voices.

The catbird fragment (figure 52) is unusual in that the dominant note or phrase is a pure sinusoid whereas the second voice, occupying only a portion of the phrase, contains harmonics of a fundamental at about 2.1 kc/s at much lower amplitude. (The amplitude per division for the two harmonics is half that for the principal phrase.)

The wood thrush (figures 53–57) is without doubt the most versatile and accomplished "internal duettist." Almost without exception the final phrase of its song involves both sources, each producing harmonically unrelated phrases with complex modulations. Figures 53 and 54 show two entire terminal phrases (by the same individual). The time-amplitude arrays were produced with the writing oscillograph; at the bottom is the corresponding sonagram at the same time scale. Figures 55 and 56 show the repetitive fragments of each phrase during a single modulating period. The extraordinary complexity of the modulation, both in amplitude and frequency, will be apparent. It is not at all difficult to hear the two voices in these terminal phrases if the recordings are played at one-eighth normal speed.

Even in the "central" or musical portion of the wood thrush song, both voices are frequently employed. Figure 57 shows the antiphonal use of the two voices to produce a rapid "trill."

The gray-cheeked thrush (figure 58) appears to have similar versatility, but I have not analyzed a sufficient number of songs to determine whether "internal duetting" is as common for this species as it is for the wood thrush.

There follows the white-necked thrush (figure 59), and two European species, the garden warbler (figure 60), and the pied flycatcher (figure 61), the latter two recorded in Sweden. Note the complex modulations in both voices for all three individuals.

For LeConte's sparrow figure 66 shows a fragment of the "buzzy" terminal portion of its song. This turns out to be two voices, each modulated in amplitude and frequency, with both modulating frequency and mean frequency at very high values.

The final example (figure 73) is a phrase from the song of a Lapland longspur, the same song which includes the phrases in figures 71 and 72, and in figure 7. Here the frequencies of the two voices are so close that it is impossible to separate them by filtration. The reciprocal periods are plotted for the unfiltered phrase and the behavior of the reciprocal period at the nodes in amplitude is uniquely characteristic of two close notes producing a beat whose period is equal to the reciprocal of the frequency difference (about 300 cycles). At the nodes the frequency rises characteristically when the amplitude of the high note is greater and drops for the reverse condition. Another curious feature is the existence of a weak fundamental for the higher of the two notes which we have shown directly below the "beating" pair.

Figure 74 is the sonagram for a portion of the Lapland longspur song, showing at (1) the sonagram for figure 7 at (2) the beating pair and the faint fundamental in figure 73, and at (3) the phrase a fragment of which is shown in figure 71.

In almost every family for which representative recordings are available, one can find cases where the two acoustical sources are simultaneously employed to produce harmonically unrelated sounds. I have, however, never observed more than two harmonically unrelated overlapping notes or phrases. To be sure there are many cases in which one sees on the sonagram a fundamental with a great many harmonics, and cases—the catbird in figure 52 for example—where one of the two sources is producing a fundamental and one or more harmonics, but these comprise harmonically *related* overlapping tones. Hence there is no basis for considering more than two sources.

It remains now to discuss the acoustical significance of these findings. We start with the premise that birds can indeed activate their two acoustical sources (the two internal tympaniform membranes) separately and individually, that this ability occurs in all groups of birds and that the ability to modulate frequency or amplitude or both is available for either source.

This evidence requires us to reject both the "musical instrument" and the "human voice" theories of avian vocalization.

In a musical instrument, as has been pointed out earlier, resonator and source are acoustically so closely coupled that the source is forced to conform in its vibrations to the harmonic spectrum of the resonator. Were the trachea and the vibrating membranes to have a similar relationship in singing birds, separate sounds from the two sources would be impossible, since both sources would be forced to conform to the tracheal resonances. We see, to the contrary, that each source can produce its own sound without apparent restriction.

The "human voice" theory presumes a source producing the equivalent of a harmonic spectrum of wide frequency range, with subsequent attenuation or reinforcement of particular portions of the spectrum through resonators, in the human case through the oral cavities. This theory does not preclude the possibility of two sources, each producing its own harmonic spectrum, but it does demand a single resonator, in the avian case the trachea, which would attenuate or reinforce only at particular frequencies. We have seen many examples in the figures associated with this section where each voice produces its own characteristic sound, nearly always sinusoidal in its wave form, and which may cover a relatively wide frequency range. It is manifestly impossible to postulate a single resonator which would produce such results through selective filtration.

We must conclude then that bird sounds are produced in their final form by the vibrating sources themselves, without further substantial modification as the sound waves pass through the trachea. The evidence thus far does not preclude modest attenuation or reinforcement of the source vibrations in the trachea, but it seems quite clear that the trachea does not change the frequency, or affect the amplitude or frequency modulation of the vibration produced at the source. The evidence for or against simple tracheal attenuation or reinforcement of the amplitude of the sound is discussed in chapter 6.

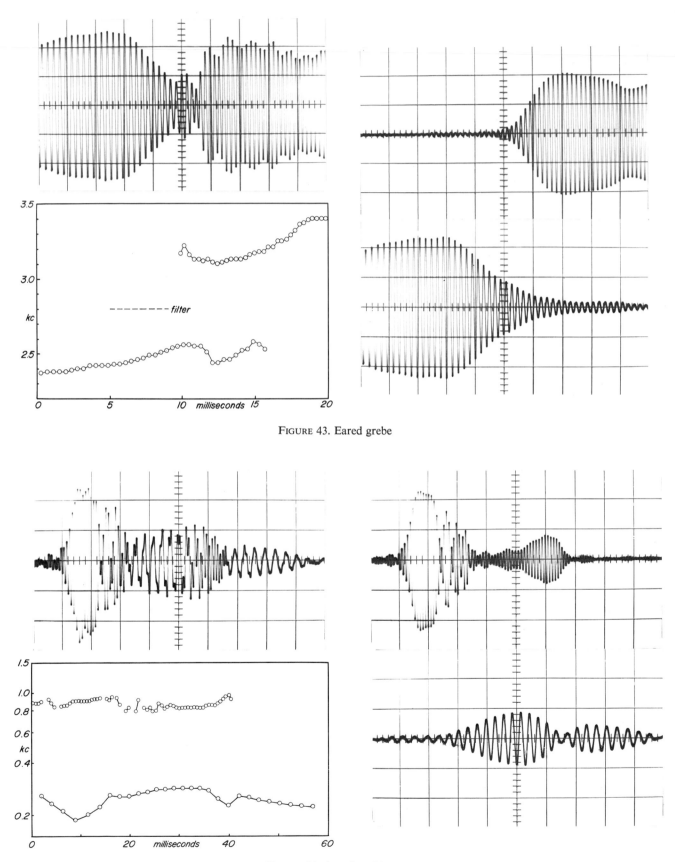

FIGURE 43. Eared grebe

FIGURE 44. American bittern

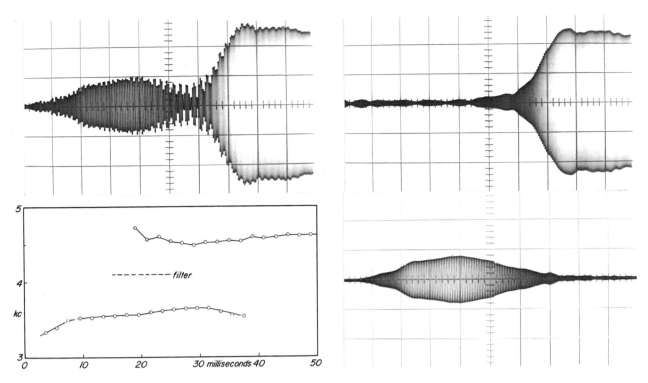

FIGURE 45. Broad-winged hawk

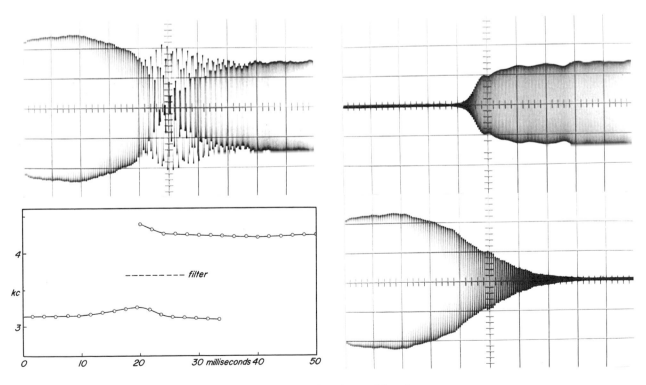

FIGURE 46. American golden plover

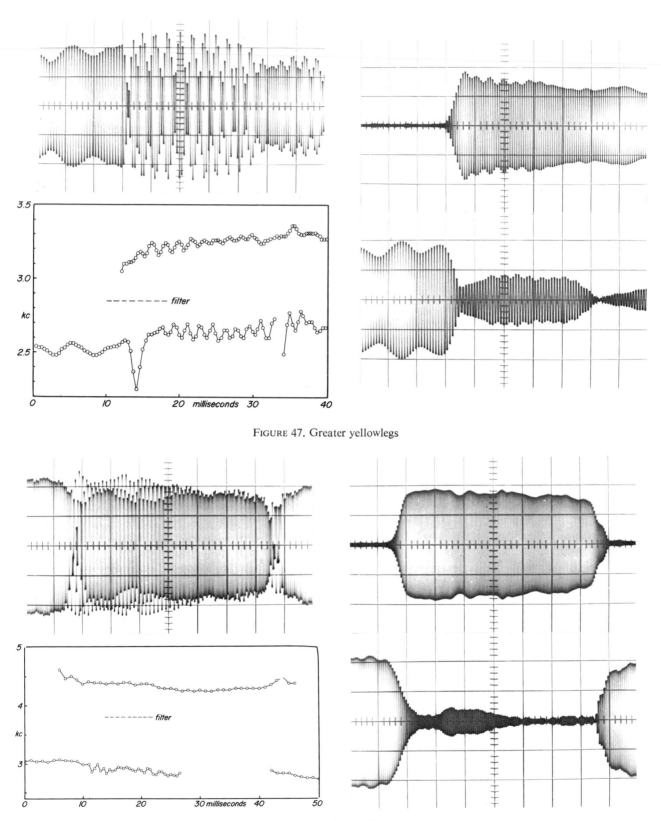

FIGURE 47. Greater yellowlegs

FIGURE 48. Red-shafted flicker

64

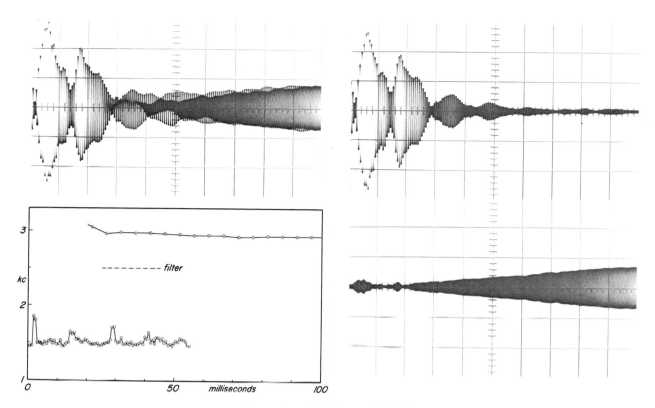

FIGURE 49. Naked-throated bellbird

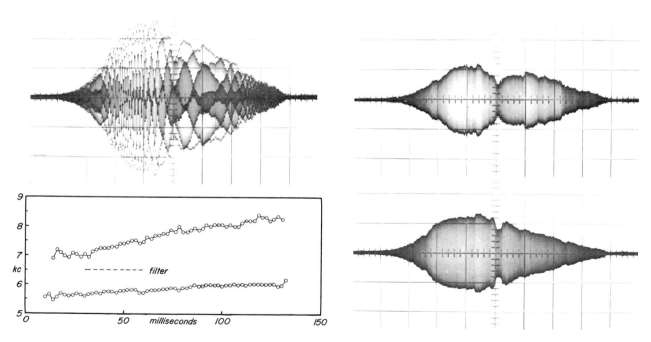

FIGURE 50. Bewick's wren

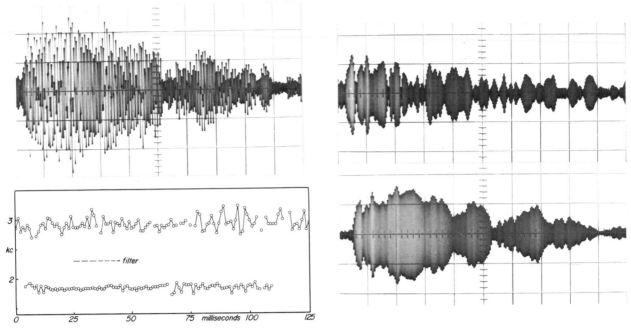

FIGURE 51. Green jay

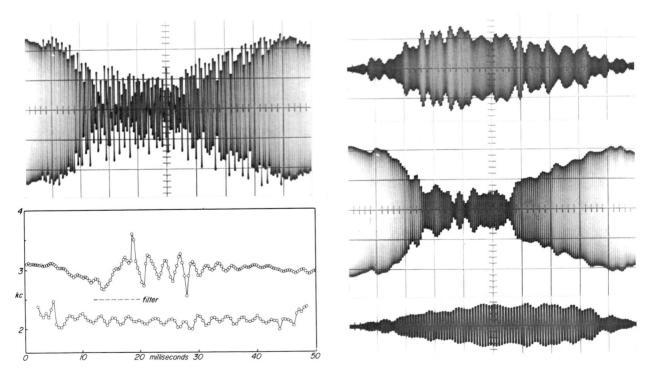

FIGURE 52. Catbird

66

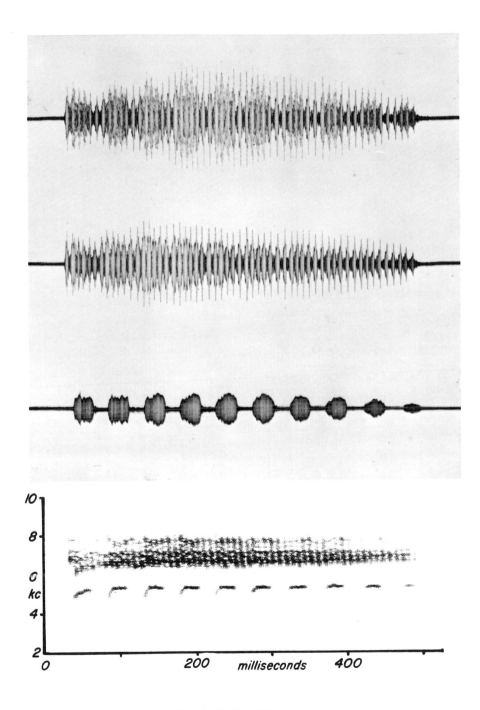

FIGURE 53. Wood thrush

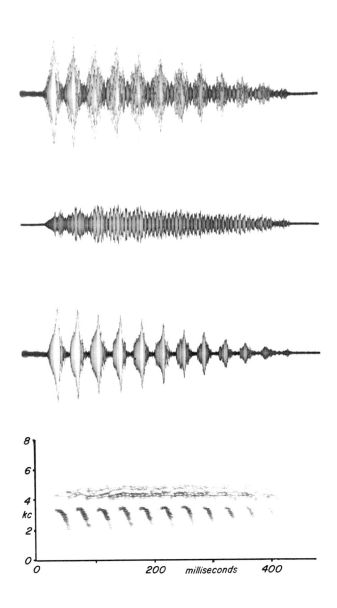

FIGURE 54. Wood thrush

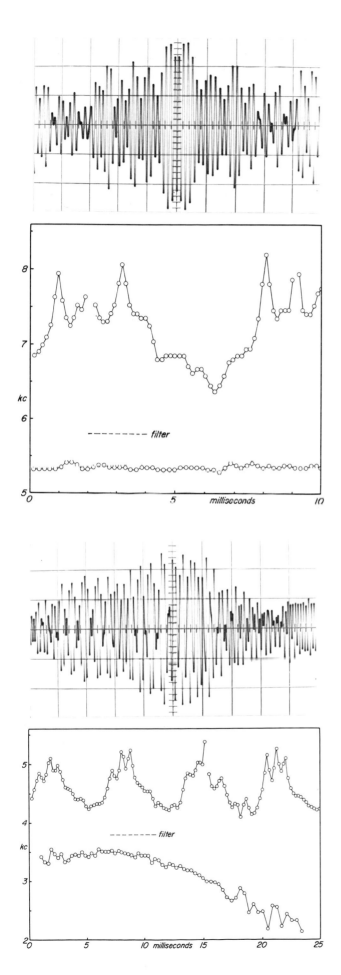

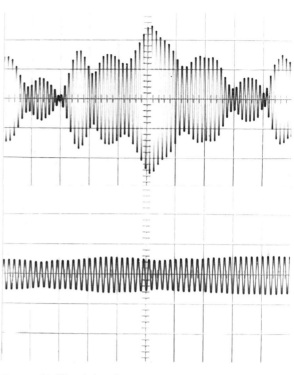

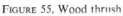

FIGURE 55. Wood thrush

FIGURE 56. Wood thrush

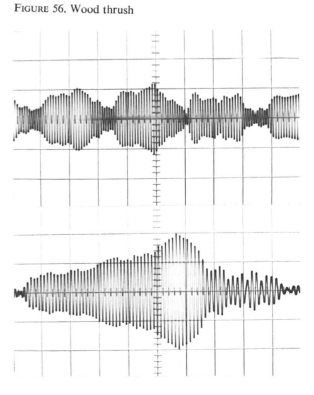

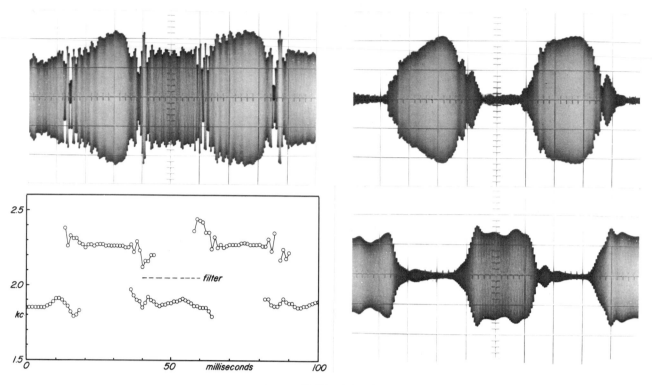

FIGURE 57. Wood thrush

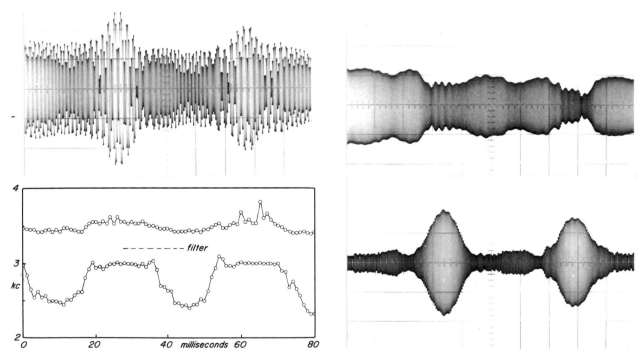

FIGURE 58. Gray-cheeked thrush

70

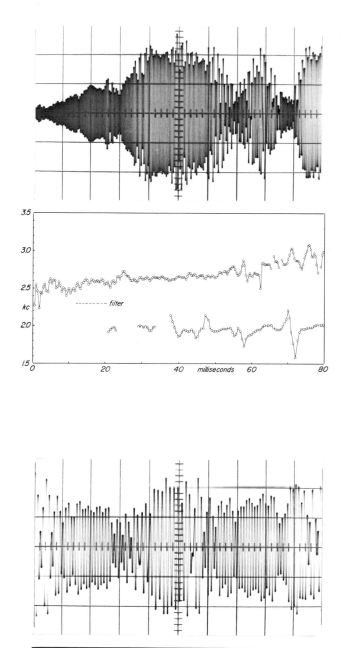

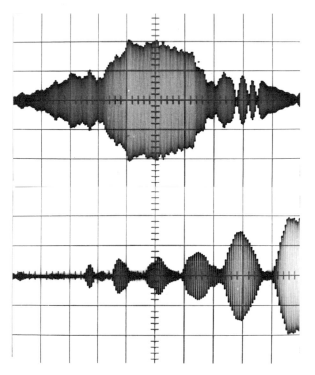

FIGURE 59. White-necked thrush

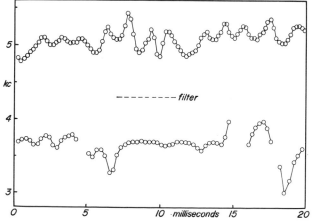

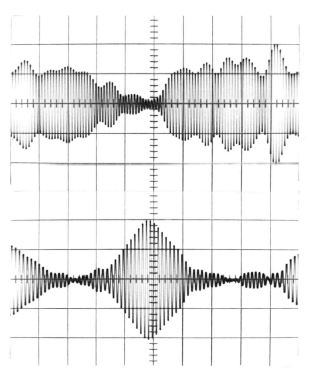

FIGURE 60. Garden warbler

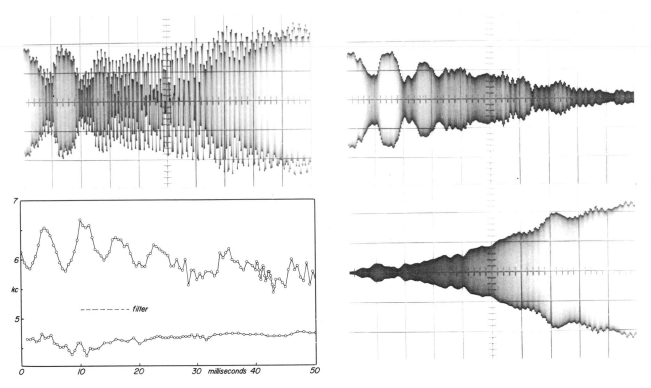

FIGURE 61. Pied flycatcher

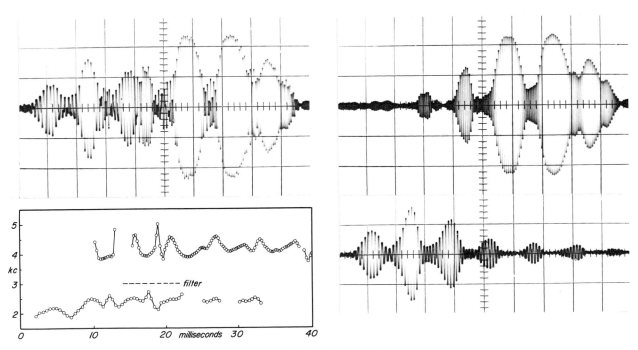

FIGURE 62. Rattling cisticola

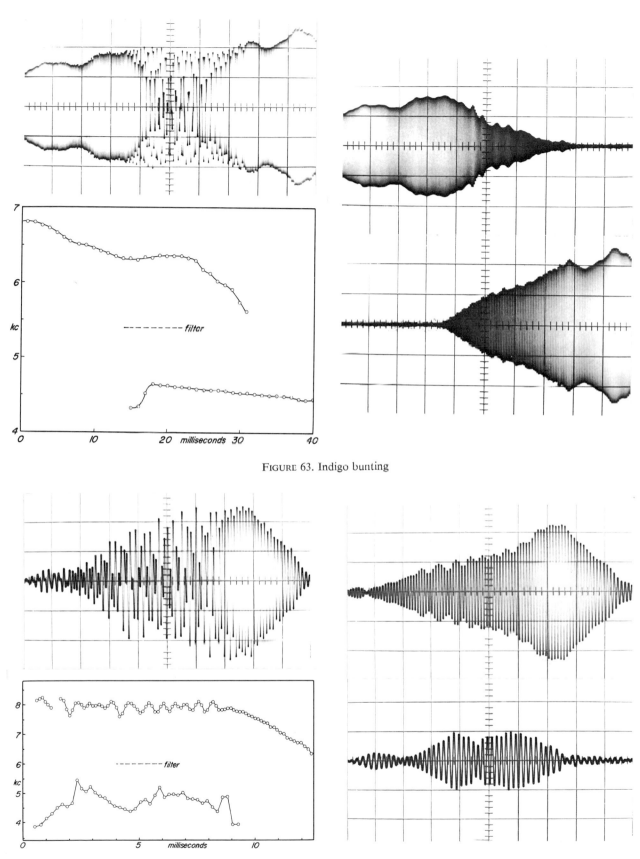

FIGURE 63. Indigo bunting

FIGURE 64. Dickcissel

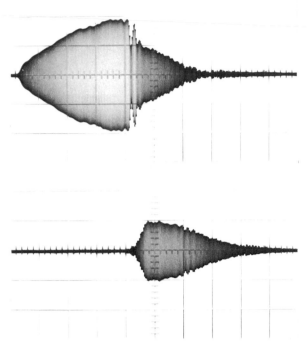

FIGURE 65. American goldfinch

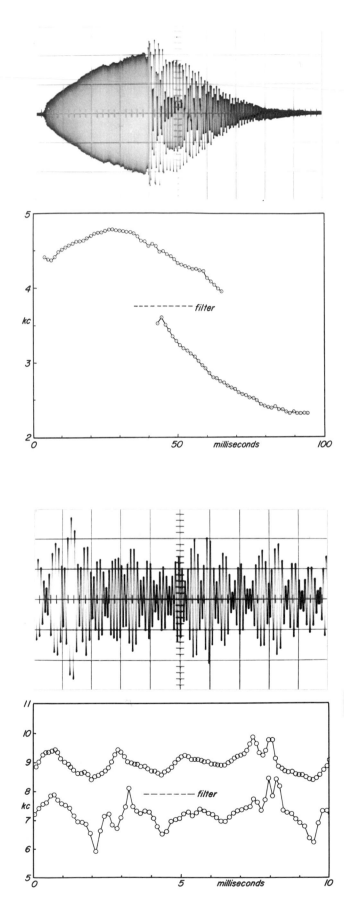

filter

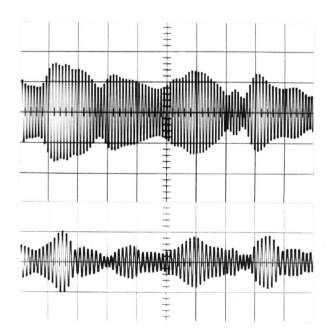

FIGURE 66. LeConte's sparrow

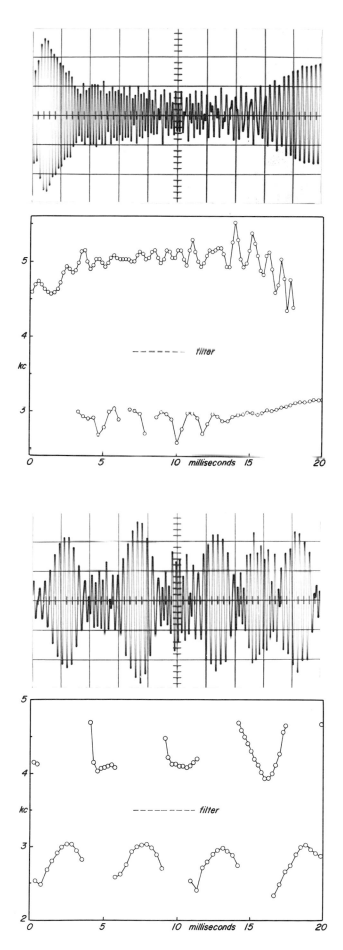

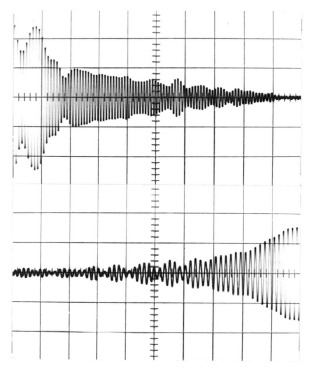

FIGURE 67. Vesper sparrow

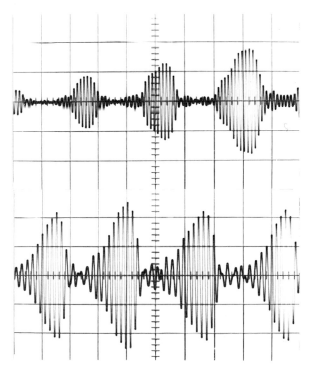

FIGURE 68. Song sparrow

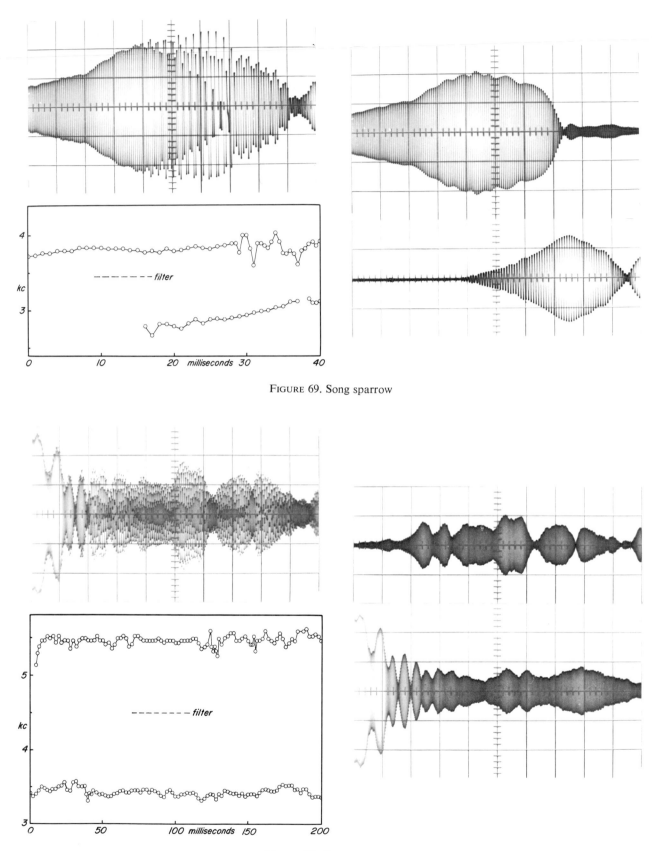

FIGURE 69. Song sparrow

FIGURE 70. Song sparrow

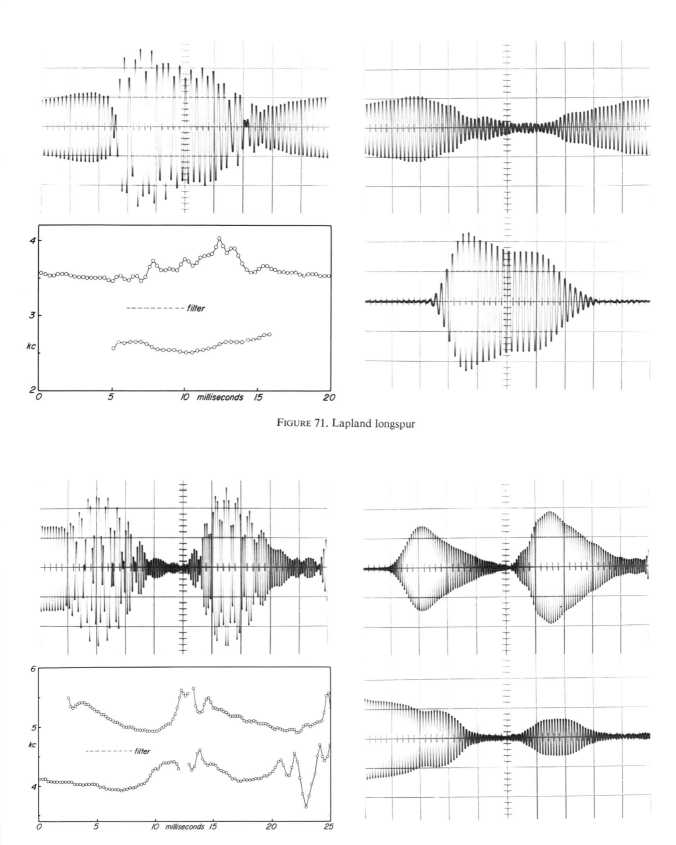

FIGURE 71. Lapland longspur

FIGURE 72. Lapland longspur

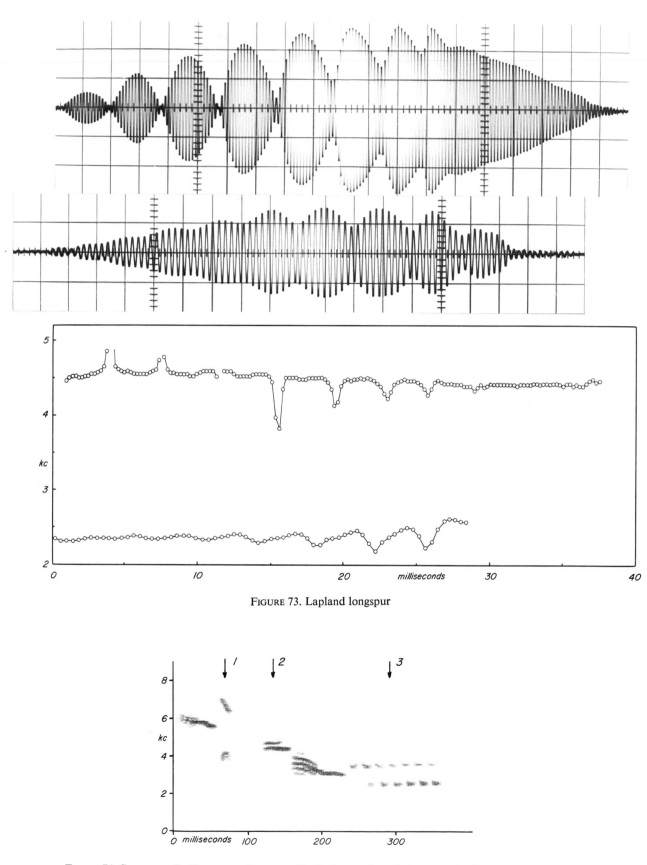

FIGURE 73. Lapland longspur

FIGURE 74. Sonagram (half tape speed, narrow filter) of a portion of the song of a Lapland longspur: 1,
phrase shown as figure 8; 2, figure 73; 3, figure 71.

Chapter 6 TRACHEAL MODULATION

In the previous chapter we have shown that bird sounds in whistled song are produced in final form at the vibrating sources, and are not controlled, or substantially modulated, by the trachea. The evidence presented does not, however, preclude the possibility of modest tracheal reinforcement at frequencies corresponding to the tracheal resonances.

Take as an example the song sparrow, whose singing range comprises the interval 2 to 8 kc/s, or two full octaves. The song sparrow's trachea is 31 mm long and has an inside diameter of about 2 mm.[5] If syrinx and trachea behave as a tube closed at one end and open at the other, resonances will be found at 2.8 and 8.5 kc/s; if they behave as a tube open at both ends the single resonance within the singing range will occur at 5.6 kc/s. For the closed tube we should find reinforcement or increased amplitude at 2.8 and 8.5 kc/s, relative attenuation at 5.6 kc/s. For the open tube we would have the converse situation; reinforcement at 5.6 kc/s, attenuation at 2.8 and 8.5 kc/s.

If, then, the trachea acts to reinforce at the resonances, we should find notes at these frequencies with amplitudes greater than average; the converse obtaining at the antiresonances.

To evaluate these possibilities sonagrams and oscillograms were prepared for 22 different song sparrow songs. In each song the (unmodulated) note of highest amplitude was given a value of 100 on an arbitrary linear scale and its frequency was

5. Peter Ames, Museum of Vertebrate Zoology, University of California, Berkeley, California. Personal communication.

recorded. For all other notes in the song we calculated the amplitude relative to 100 and recorded the corresponding frequency. The results for the 22 songs are shown in figure 75. Were the trachea attenuating at the antiresonances we should find all notes at these frequencies to have lower than average amplitudes, i.e., at 5.6 kc for the closed tube case; at 2.8 and 8.5 kc for the open tube. The figure shows no such "forbidden" frequencies; in fact most frequencies within the singing range can be found in the interval 90–100 percent of maximum amplitude. There appears a small gap between 5.6 and 6.4 kc but I suspect this would be filled if a greater number of songs had been examined; in any event we find the gap closed if we drop to 70 percent of maximum amplitude.

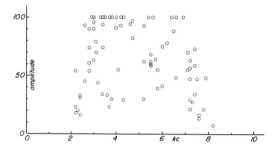

FIGURE 75. Song sparrows. Relative amplitude vs frequency for 22 songs. For each song the note of highest amplitude was taken as 100%, the other notes as a percentage of the maximum. Note that there appear to be no "forbidden" frequencies, viz., the entire range of 2.5 to 7.5 kc is represented in the 90–100% amplitude region.

There is, to be sure, a sharp fall in amplitude at the extremes of the singing range and since the terminal frequencies correspond approximately to the antiresonance values for the open tube case, one might assume these to be responsible for the termination of the singing range. Such an assumption would, however, imply an exceedingly inefficient tracheal filter, since its band width would approximate 5 kc/s (in human speech the band widths for the oral cavities at the formant frequencies range from 50 to 250 c/s). It is much more reasonable to assume that the singing range is determined not by tracheal resonances but by some other physiological phenomenon, perhaps by the permissible tensions in the tympanic membranes.

We conclude then that tracheal reinforcement or attenuation, at least for the song sparrow, is minimal, and not a significant factor controlling its song. Unfortunately such an analysis is possible for only a few species, since not many have the song sparrows' extended range (or the willingness to use it).

A second method for appraising tracheal modulation comprises the examination of glissandi which cover a substantial frequency range. For if the glissando traverses a tracheal resonance or antiresonance we should see a marked increase or decrease in amplitude at the appropriate frequencies. Here also there are difficulties; for while glissandi are quite common in the songs of many species, they are usually of short duration, so short in fact that ambiguities are introduced by the rise and fall in amplitude at the beginning and end of the note.

Diligent search has, however, uncovered a few cases in which the phrase is long enough to avoid terminal ambiguities, and in which the glissando covers approximately an octave. These are shown in figures 76–79. Consider, for example, the yellow warbler, figure 76. The phrase embraces a full octave (4 to 8 kc/s), and while

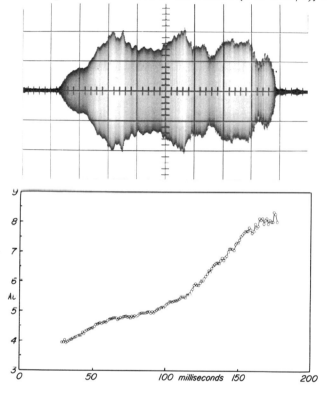

FIGURE 76. Glissando: yellow warbler

there are changes in amplitude, these in an acoustical sense are very small (less than 3 db) and it is most unlikely that they are associated with resonances. The two amplitude minima at 90 and 130 msec, for example, correspond to frequencies at 4.8 and 6.5 kc/s. One of these could correspond to a resonance, both could not. The same comments are appropriate for the chestnut-sided warbler (figure 77) and for the American goldfinch (figure 78).

The song sparrow (figure 79) shows two phenomena; the simultaneous use of both acoustical sources, and a glissando in one of the voices extending over an octave. Here the amplitude during the glissando is almost constant, excepting of course for the periodic amplitude modulation which occurs during the flat portion of the frequency curve. [Note that placement of the filter, to isolate the upper voice from the lower, cuts through the upper voice at its low frequency termination. Inspection of the two oscillograms at the right of the figure gives a rough idea of the efficiency of the filter.]

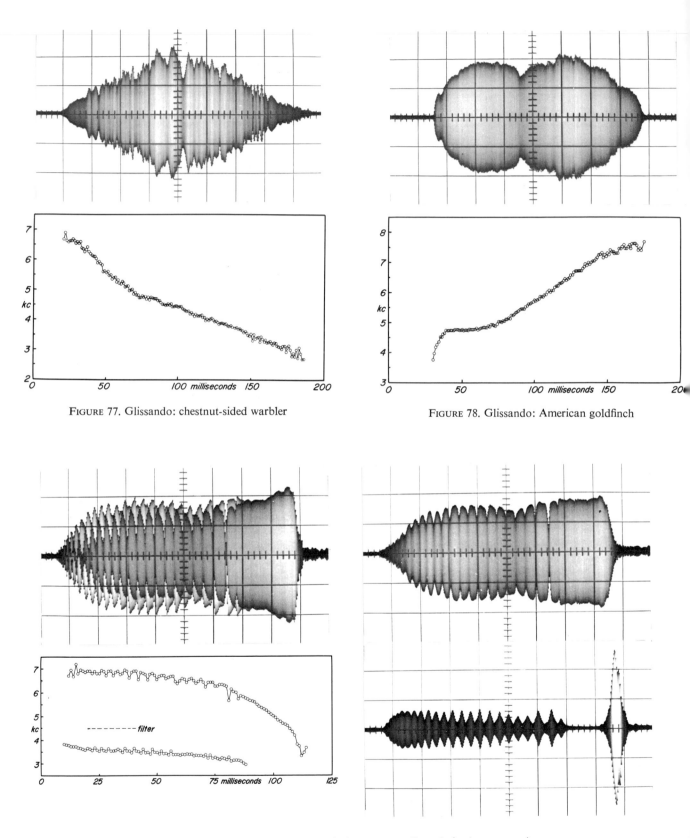

FIGURE 77. Glissando: chestnut-sided warbler

FIGURE 78. Glissando: American goldfinch

FIGURE 79. Song sparrow. Two acoustical sources, a glissando in the upper voice.

These two sets of experiments, the song sparrow series and the glissandi, indicate strongly that the trachea is without significant effect in modulating the vibrations arising from the source. The evidence would of course have been much more impressive had it been possible to include a greater number of species. This has not been possible since long glissandi are rare, and few species have the virtuosity of the song sparrow in terms of range and variety.

It remains now to determine whether there is a valid acoustical basis for these rather surprising observations. For the trachea is after all a tube; a tube, if its losses are small, exhibits resonances, and one would expect such a tube to be an effective modulator, even though lack of rigidity in its construction should give rise to substantial damping.

For the exposition which follows I am indebted to Mr. J. L. Flanagan of the Bell Telephone Laboratories to whom I express sincere appreciation as well for the time he has given so generously in introducing me into the mysteries of acoustical mathematics.

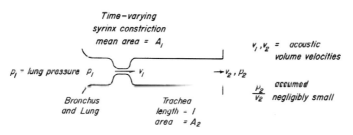

FIGURE 80. Simplified syrinx model.

Figure 80 shows a simplified model of the avian vocal apparatus. The syrinx constriction is due to the inward bulge of the tympaniform membrane resulting from the pressure external to the bronchus produced in the clavicular sac. Air flow (v_1) through the constriction induces vibrations in the membrane producing in turn the time-varying cross-sectional area A_1. The lung pressure p_1 provides the driving force for the air flow. The cross-sectional area of the bronchus is assumed to be large compared to the syrinx constriction. The trachea is a tube of constant cross-sectional area A_2 and length ℓ.

We assume the flow through the syrinx constriction to be in the turbulent region and that the familiar flow formula will have a discharge coefficient of unity. Then

$$v_1 \simeq \left[\frac{2p_1}{\rho}\right]^{1/2} \times A_1,$$

where

ρ is the air density,
p_1 is the lung pressure (above atmospheric pressure),
A_1 is the mean area of the syrinx constriction,
v_1 is the mean volume velocity through the syrinx.

The acoustical syrinx impedance R is assumed to be purely resistive, and given by the kinetic energy per unit volume of air due to acceleration by a constant lung pressure p_1. Then

$$R \simeq \frac{(2\rho p_1)^{1/2}}{A_1}.$$

Tracheal losses are assumed to be small[6] as compared with R, hence the tracheal impedance will be purely reactive.

We assume also that the radiation impedance at the anterior end of the trachea will be negligibly small. As justification for this assumption we point out that for song birds the wave lengths included within their singing range are large with respect to the tracheal radius. The song sparrow, for example, has a frequency range 2 to 8 kc/s and a tracheal radius of about one millimeter. The ratio wave length to tracheal radius thus ranges from 45 to 180. Under these circumstances the ratio of pressure to volume velocity (p_2/v_2) at the anterior (open) end of the trachea will be very small, and the radiation impedance will have negligible effect on the volume velocity through the trachea. Hence *for the calculation of tracheal transmission,* the radiation impedance can be neglected, and the system can be simplified by assuming, in effect, a "pressure short circuit" at the tracheal termination.

We may now construct an electrical analog for the acoustical system, representing the trachea by the familiar T circuit (figure 81).

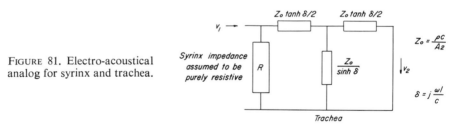

FIGURE 81. Electro-acoustical analog for syrinx and trachea.

The acoustic inductance L and capacitance C per unit tracheal length will be

$$L \simeq \rho/A_2,$$
$$C \simeq A_2/\rho c_2,$$

and

$$Z_0 = \left[\frac{L}{C}\right]^{1/2} = \frac{\rho c}{A_2},$$

where

c is the velocity of sound,
ρ is the air density,
A_2 is the cross-sectional area of the trachea.

6. Such calculations as can be made, i.e., for heat conduction and viscosity, support this assumption. The losses are finite, but small as compared to the damping and matching due to the syrinx.

From transmission line theory we have

$$v_2^1(\omega) = v_1^1(\omega)\left[\frac{1}{\cosh \delta + Z_0/R \sinh \delta}\right],$$

where v_2^1 and v_1^1 are the time-varying (alternating) components of the volume velocity; the constant component of the flow affecting only the calculation of syrinx impedance, and (for the lossless trachea) δ is the imaginary argument $j \omega\ell/c$ (where ω is the radian frequency, equal to $2\pi f$).

Converting from hyperbolic to circular functions and setting

$$T(\omega) = \frac{v_2^1(\omega)}{v_1^1(\omega)} = \begin{array}{l}\text{the frequency-dependent}\\ \text{relative transmission of}\\ \text{the system,}\end{array}$$

we have

$$T(\omega) = \frac{1}{\cos \omega\ell/c + j Z_0/R \sin \omega\ell/c}.$$

From this equation it is evident that when $R = Z_0$, $T(\omega)$ becomes unity; hence there will be no tracheal attenuation or reinforcement at any frequency.

Figure 82 shows the variation in relative transmission with θ for selected values of the ratio Z_0/R where $\theta = \omega\ell/c$ radians and frequency $= c\theta/2\pi\ell$.

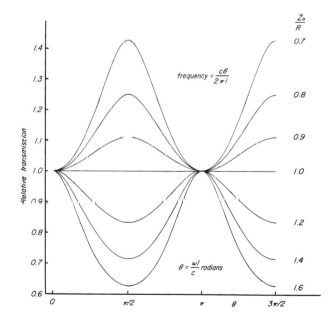

FIGURE 82. Relative transmission as a function of frequency and the impedance ratio trachea to syrinx.

We see that for values of this ratio below unity ($R > Z_0$) the system behaves more nearly as a tube closed at one end, and open at the other, with maximum transmission (closed tube resonances) at odd multiples of $\theta = \pi/2$, or at frequencies which are odd multiples of $c/4\ell$. For Z_0/R equal to unity, there is no reinforcement or attenuation; when the ratio exceeds unity ($R < Z_0$) the system behaves much as a tube open at both ends with maximum transmission at integer multiples of $\theta = \pi$ or at frequencies which are multiples of integer $c/2\ell$.

We can express the ratio Z_0/R in terms of A_1 and A_2 as follows:

$$Z_0/R = A_1/A_2 \times \frac{\rho c}{\sqrt{2\rho p_1}}$$

We must first select an appropriate value for p_1, the lung pressure. I have found no published values for the lung pressure in singing birds; hence as a rough approximation we may use the values determined for humans when speaking. This pressure ranges from 4 to 20 cm of water and one might guess that 8 cm of water lung pressure would be appropriate for a singing bird. Taking, in consistent (cgs) units,

$$\rho = 1.14 \times 10^{-3}$$
$$c = 3.5 \times 10^{4}$$
$$p_1 = 8 \times 980$$
$$Z_0/R = 9.5\ A_1/A_2 .$$

Hence Z_0 will equal R when the tracheal cross-sectional area is 9.5 times the mean syringeal cross-sectional area.

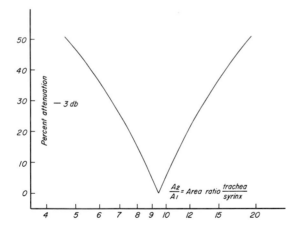

FIGURE 83. Maximum tracheal attenuation as a function of the cross-sectional area ratio trachea to syrinx.

Figure 83 shows maximum (relative) attenuation as a function of the area ratio. Maximum attenuation is 100 minus the ratio (expressed as a percentage) of the minimum to the maximum transmission. We see that between area ratios of 6.8 and 13.5 (a factor 2) the maximum attenuation will be less than 30 per cent, which would appear to give the bird adequate flexibility in avoiding frequencies and amplitudes where tracheal attenuation would be substantial.

Finally we can make a rough appraisal, using the song sparrow as an example, of the reasonableness of these assumptions by calculating the air flow required while singing. We take the tracheal radius as one millimeter and assume the mean syringeal cross-section to be one-tenth the tracheal cross-section (the point determined above at which there will be no tracheal attenuation or reinforcement). Taking the lung pressure at 8 cm water, we calculate the volume velocity from the equation

$$v_1 = \left[\frac{2p_1}{\rho}\right]^{\frac{1}{2}} \times A_1$$

to be 12 cm^3 of air per second.

The average song sparrow song lasts about 2.5 sec, and sound is produced roughly half the time. Hence the total air expenditure for a typical song would be 15 cm^3, which seems an eminently reasonable result.

We recognize, of course, that many of the assumptions involved in these calculations may be in error, and the true matching impedances may correspond to area ratios, trachea to syrinx, on either side of the value 9.5. The important point is that there *will* be an area ratio where R equals Z_0 and tracheal modulation will be minimal over a fair range of area ratios on either side of the matching ratio.

One final comment. The necks of birds (which contain and limit the trachea) have many functions requiring a considerable degree of flexibility; feeding, for example, preening, sight over a large circular angle, nest building, and perhaps others. It would be odd indeed if these purely functional uses should operate to restrict freedom in so important an activity as song. It is much more reasonable to think that nature, with her customary ingenuity, has devised singing mechanisms which leave the neck and head free to perform other important functions without interference. However valid this argument, it would seem clear that, at least for whistled song, the trachea does not significantly modulate the sounds produced at the source.

Chapter 7   MODULATIONS: REAL AND SPURIOUS

A characteristic of bird song, particularly of whistled song, is the extremely rapid repetitive rise and fall, of both amplitude and frequency, found in certain phrases or notes. It is tempting to assume that all such manifestations, which appear superficially to be modulations, arise from the same acoustical or physiological mechanism. Unfortunately this seems not to be the case and it becomes necessary to undertake more searching analysis to determine which of these phenomena are true modulations and which are not.

With the Sonagraph, such phenomena appear as a series of two or more frequencies separated by a constant frequency interval. With the oscilloscope one sees a train of sinusoidal waves included within a periodically recurring amplitude envelope. Neither of these manifestations standing alone permits unambiguous decision as to whether one has a true modulation or whether some other phenomenon is involved.

We define true modulation in bird song as the superposition, on a phrase of constant amplitude and frequency, of a modifying process which changes amplitude or frequency or both. This modulating process may or may not be periodic, and the mechanisms producing the phrase of constant frequency and amplitude on the one hand, and the modulation on the other, must be physically unrelated.

It is possible to specify four mechanisms, which give rise to superficially similar arrays on Sonagraph and oscilloscope, only one of which is a true modulation.

In this chapter we describe these four mechanisms and the specific criteria for distinguishing between them, and show an example taken from typical bird songs for each of the four types.

A Phrase with Beats (Case I)

Such a phrase is produced when two notes are generated simultaneously, one in each acoustical source. The situation can be expressed mathematically as follows:

$$A(t) = a \cos 2 \pi f_1 t + b \cos 2 \pi f_2 t$$

where f_1 and f_2 are the two source frequencies, a and b their amplitudes, and $A(t)$ the instantaneous amplitude. If the two source amplitudes are equal (a = b) the wave form is specified by the equation

$$A(t) = 2 a \cos 2 \pi t \left[\frac{f_1 + f_2}{2} \right] \times \cos 2 \pi t \left[\frac{f_1 - f_2}{2} \right]$$

We see that the wave will comprise a train of sinusoids whose frequency will equal the mean of the source frequencies. Upon this is superimposed an apparent amplitude modulation whose frequency will be the *difference* between the source frequencies.

Unfortunately a true amplitude modulation, superimposed upon a single source-generated carrier frequency, produces a superficially similar wave form; hence criteria must be developed which will distinguish unequivocally between the two manifestations. These are as follows:

Where a beat phenomenon is involved the wave analyzer (or sonagram) will show energy at only the two source frequencies. True amplitude modulation, on the other hand, will show energy at *three* frequencies, viz., at the carrier or source frequency, and at two "side-band" frequencies placed above and below the carrier and separated from it by intervals equal to the modulating frequency.

For a sinusoidal amplitude modulation the wave form and side-band frequencies are specified by the equations:

$$A(t) = a \cos 2 \pi f_1 t (1 + m \cos 2 \pi f_2 t)$$

$$= a \cos 2 \pi f_1 t + \frac{a\,m}{2} [\cos 2 \pi t (f_1 + f_2) + \cos 2 \pi t (f_1 - f_2)],$$

where f_1 and f_2 are carrier and modulating frequencies, respectively, a and m are the amplitudes of carrier and modulating frequencies, and $A(t)$ the instantaneous amplitude.

For beats the mean frequency of the wave form will fall between the source frequencies, whereas for amplitude modulation the mean frequency must by definition correspond precisely to the carrier frequency as determined with the wave analyzer.

For amplitude modulation the period[7] for individual sinusoids within the repeating

7. Period is defined as the time interval between successive points of zero amplitude on the rising limbs of a sinusoidal wave. The reciprocal of the period is the "instantaneous" frequency. It should be understood that "instantaneous" frequency has no real significance. It is, however, convenient to plot frequencies rather than periods since the term frequency is more readily understood. Futhermore, if the frequency (reciprocal period) remains constant or changes slowly over a significant time interval, the phenomenon becomes psychologically real. We should emphasize that the "significant time interval" is undoubtedly shorter for birds than for humans.

wave form will be constant. For beats there will be a sharp change in period at amplitude minima. At these minima the period may rise or fall depending on the relative amplitudes of the two sources, and also on their phase relationships. If, for example, the low frequency source has the higher amplitude the period will *rise* (the frequency will fall) at amplitude minima. If the high frequency source has the high amplitude the converse will appear.

For beats the amplitude envelope corresponding to the "modulating" period should have a sinusoidal form; for amplitude modulations the envelope may or may not be sinusoidal, depending on the mechanism producing the modulation.

Source-generated Modulations (Case II)

Such modulations arise when there is superimposed on a "carrier" frequency a periodic change in frequency, or amplitude, or both. In bird song, as we shall see later, frequency and amplitude modulation almost always occur together; only in rare cases can we find pure amplitude or pure frequency modulation. Hence it becomes easier to distinguish "modulations" from "beats," but less easy to distinguish "modulations" from certain types of harmonic spectra.

The mathematics of frequency or amplitude modulation are straightforward when the modulation has a sinusoidal envelope, but for bird song this is rarely the case, and mathematical analysis of side-band amplitudes is of little use. All one can say is that such modulations give rise to a series of side bands above and below the carrier frequency spaced at intervals equal to the modulating frequency.

The criteria for such modulations are as follows:

The mean period of the sinusoids comprising the modulation will be the exact reciprocal of the carrier frequency as determined with wave analyzer or Sonagraph.

Since the modulating mechanism (e.g., the syringeal muscles) is unrelated to the source of the carrier frequency (the tympanic membrane) the carrier or side-band frequencies will *not* necessarily be integer multiples of the modulating frequency.[8]

Successive periods *within* the modulating period will vary regularly (but not necessarily sinusoidally) between maxima and minima. There will be no irregular or sharp changes from one period to the next.

The carrier frequency may be found at any frequency within the singing range of the bird.

A Source-generated Harmonic Spectrum (Case III)

The source (the tympanic membrane) will vibrate to produce an harmonic spectrum. Its nature will depend on membrane thickness and on the value of the tension-controlled fundamental frequency.

8. It is possible by sheer coincidence for carrier or side-band frequencies to be integer multiples of the modulating frequency. There is no a priori requirement that this be so.

As we shall see later, there appears to be a threshold frequency (for a given bird) below which harmonics will appear. As the fundamental frequency decreases below this threshold value the lower harmonics tend to be gradually suppressed, the higher harmonics to be emphasized. The result may be a wave form superficially resembling a source-generated modulation. When the fundamental is very low the lower harmonics virtually disappear, and the distinction between the two phenomena presents serious interpretive difficulties. There are, however, the following criteria:

The wave forms arising from such an harmonic spectrum will be precisely repetitive, both as to amplitude and period, within the apparent modulating period, so long as the fundamental frequency and the signal amplitude remain constant.

Successive periods will not vary smoothly within the modulation but may show sharp changes either toward higher or lower values. One will frequently find periods which have lost their sinusoidal form.

The frequency of any harmonic must be an integer multiple of the apparent modulating frequency.[9]

It is a fortunate fact that harmonic spectra in bird song quite often contain a single harmonic having substantially greater amplitude than any of its near neighbors. Under these circumstances the repeating wave form (the apparent modulation) will comprise sinusoids whose mean period is precisely the reciprocal of the frequency of the dominant harmonic. Such a situation provides a ready means of distinguishing between this case III and cases II and IV, for in neither of these latter situations will the "carrier" frequency be an integer multiple of the modulating frequency.

The amplitude envelope of the "modulation" may take almost any form. The form will, however, be less regular and less nearly sinusoidal than one would see for either cases I or II.

Source-generated Pulses Modulated by a Tracheal Resonance (Case IV)

This is the mechanism involved in human speech, the larynx providing the pulsed source, the oral and nasal cavities the resonator. In birds the source becomes the syrinx, the resonator the trachea. It is entirely possible, from a physiological point of view, for birds to vocalize using this mechanism, but I have found no example where it is unambiguously clear that this is the case. We can, however, set down criteria which should distinguish this mechanism from the other types of real or apparent modulation.

A periodically pulsed air flow at the syringeal source will be equivalent by Fourier analysis to a harmonic spectrum whose characteristics will depend on the ratio—pulse duration to the interval between pulses (the duty factor)—and to the shape of

9. Implicit in this statement is the assumption that vibrating membranes will in fact produce harmonics which are integer multiples of the fundamental frequency. There are cases, such as the piano and the ringing of bells, for which this is not so. As we show later, the assumption is valid for bird song.

the pulse. If, for example, the pulse is of infinitely short duration, the harmonic spectrum will extend to infinite frequency without decay in amplitude. As the duty factor increases the rate of amplitude decay increases. In all cases the frequency of the fundamental will be the reciprocal of the interval between successive pulses.

When such a pulsed source is associated with a resonator we will have reinforcement of those pulse harmonics which are embraced within the resonance or resonances, and attenuation of the remainder of the pulse spectrum. It follows then that the final wave form will comprise a train of sinusoids whose mean period will be the reciprocal of the resonance frequencies.

If the system behaves as a tube open at both ends resonances will appear at frequencies having wave lengths equal to 2/1, 2/2, 2/3, etc., the length of the tube; if we have the equivalent of a tube closed at one end and open at the other, the frequencies will have wave lengths 4/1, 4/3, 4/5, etc., the length of the tube. For a given bird the wave forms will be restricted to trains of damped sinusoids at these particular frequencies.

There will of course be a *series* of resonances whose frequencies will be related as 1:2:3 for the open tube, or as 1:3:5 for the closed tube. Should the source spectrum decay with sufficient rapidity (a pulse with a high duty factor) one may have a situation in which only the first resonance is observed.

Since tracheal resonances will not be equal to particular harmonics of the pulsed source there will (in general) be no integer relationship between the resonance frequency and the fundamental frequency of the pulse.[10]

The amplitude of the signal within a "modulating" period will decay exponentially, the rate of decay depending on the damping characteristics of the resonator.

To meet these tests, then, we would expect to see a wave form apparently modulated at intervals corresponding to the pulse frequency, its amplitude decaying exponentially within the "modulating" period, and comprising trains of sinusoids whose mean period corresponds to the resonance frequency. The first resonance must also have a frequency corresponding to a wave length 2 or 4 times the tracheal length.

Examples, taken from bird songs, for each of these four acoustical mechanisms follow.

Beat Notes

Figure 84 shows a 10-msec fragment taken from a phrase in the song of a Lapland longspur (the oscillogram for the entire phrase is shown as figure 73, the sonagram on figure 74). Figure 84 is the oscillogram showing amplitude as a function of time. At the bottom are shown the reciprocals of successive periods (instantaneous frequencies) for the individual sinusoids in the time-amplitude array. The dashed lines

10. Here again there is the possibility that an integer relationship will be found, but such a finding would be purely coincidental.

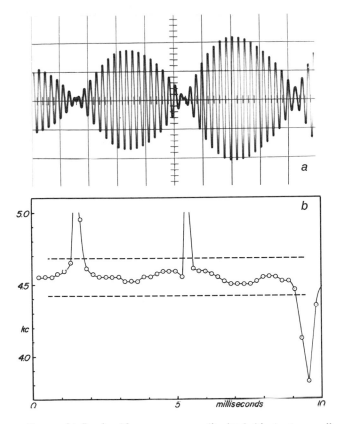

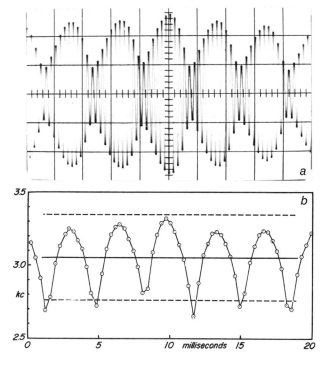

FIGURE 84. Lapland longspur: *a*, amplitude; *b*, "instantaneous" frequencies. The dashed lines are the frequencies of the two voices.

FIGURE 86. A 20-msec fragment of the phrase shown in figure 85: *a*, amplitude; *b*, "instantaneous" frequencies. The solid line is the carrier; the dashed lines the first pair of side bands.

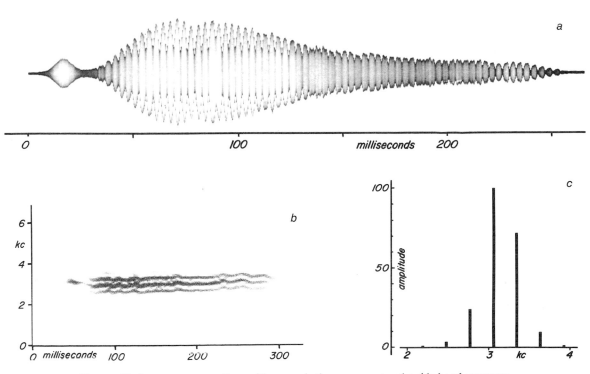

FIGURE 85. Song sparrow: *a*, the oscillogram; *b*, the sonagram; *c*, the side-band spectrum.

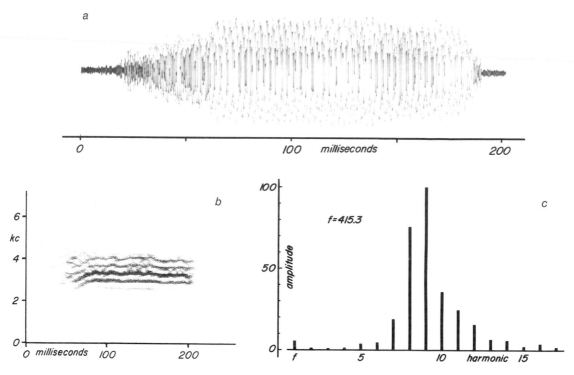

FIGURE 87. Black-capped chickadee phrase from scold call: *a*, the oscillogram; *b*, the sonagram; *c*, the harmonic spectrum.

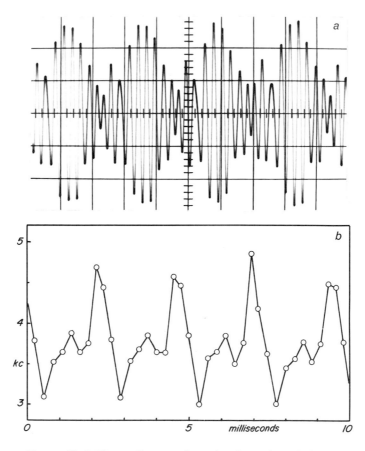

FIGURE 88. A 10-msec fragment from the phrase shown in figure 87:
a, amplitude; *b*, "instantaneous" frequencies.

are the frequencies of the two voices measured by setting filters to embrace each voice successively, and determining the time interval for 100 successive sinusoidal periods. The frequencies are found to be 4683 and 4422 c/s, respectively, the difference, 261 c/s, corresponding closely to the time interval between amplitude minima (the mean interval for five successive minima corresponds to 263 c/s).

We see that the frequency of the unfiltered phrase lies between the two voice frequencies. We note also the sharp rise in frequency at amplitude minima for the first two notes. Careful examination of the time-amplitude array shows a phase change characteristic of beat notes when the amplitudes of the two voices are equal. At the third minimum the amplitude of the lower of the two voices has increased relatively; hence the frequency here falls. We note finally the rectified sinusoidal character of the amplitude envelopes. All criteria for a beat note appear to be satisfied.

A Source-generated Modulation

Figure 85 shows a modulated phrase from the song of a song sparrow: a, the oscillogram, b, the sonagram, and c, the side-band and carrier amplitudes determined using the wave analyzer. Figure 86 shows a 20-msec fragment of this phrase: a, is the time-amplitude, and b, the time-frequency array determined as described above for the longspur. The solid horizontal line is the carrier frequency, the two dashed lines the first pair of side bands.

The carrier and side-band frequencies determined by filtration are 3062, 3353, and 2775 c/s, respectively. The mean frequency determined without filtration is 3060 c/s, in excellent agreement with the filtered value. Carrier-side-band differences are 291 and 287 c/s, in good agreement with 290 c/s obtained by taking the mean of nine intervals between amplitude minima. Neither carrier nor side-band frequencies are integer multiples of the modulating frequency (the values are 11.6, 10.6, and 9.6, respectively); hence they cannot be harmonics of a fundamental at 290 c/s.

The phrase also shows the simultaneous occurrence of frequency and amplitude modulation, both having the same modulating frequency. Neither frequency nor amplitude envelopes have a true sinusoidal form; note for example the relatively sharp drop in frequency at amplitude minima.

A Source-generated Harmonic Spectrum

Figure 87 shows a phrase from the scold call of a black-capped chickadee: a is the oscillogram; b, the corresponding sonagram; c, the harmonic spectrum made using the wave analyzer. The three figures are quite generally similar to those obtained from source-generated modulations.

Figure 88 shows a 10-msec fragment of this phrase: a, showing the time-amplitude array; b, a plot of reciprocal period (instantaneous frequency) for successive sinusoids. Note the precise correspondence of the "modulating period" in both frequency and amplitude arrays, the irregularity of the frequency figures, and finally the fact that some of the individual waves, particularly those corresponding to minimum frequency, show a substantial departure from a sinusoidal form.

I have isolated by filtration the five high amplitude harmonics and have measured their frequency from the time interval for 100 successive periods. The results are given in table 1.

TABLE 1

Harmonic Number (a)	Measured Frequency c/s (b)	(b)/(a)
7	2901	414.5
8	3320	415.0
9	3739	415.4
10	4159	415.9
11	4573	415.7
Mean value for fundamental frequency		415.3

The values for the fundamental frequency are seen to be in close agreement between themselves and with the value 415.7 c/s obtained by averaging the values for twelve successive "modulating" periods taken from the unfiltered time-frequency array.

The mean frequency of the unfiltered sinusoids, 3741 c/s, coincides almost exactly with the measured frequency of the ninth harmonic. This is due to the substantially higher amplitude of this harmonic as compared with the amplitudes of the other harmonics.

The "modulating" period contains nine sinusoids, each of them having periods which are nearly identical for successive modulating periods, as can be seen in table 2. Here we show the mean value for successive periods in twelve "modulating" periods; the standard deviation σ, and σ as a percentage of the mean period.

TABLE 2

No.	Microseconds p_m	σ	σ/p_m %
1	339.8	5.1	1.51
2	279.2	3.2	1.14
3	274.6	1.9	0.70
4	263.4	1.9	0.72
5	277.3	3.0	1.06
6	272.2	2.7	1.00
7	225.7	7.1	3.15
8	219.8	6.7	3.03
9	254.3	7.5	2.95
Σ	2405.7	10.3	0.43

We see that the values for the individual periods are quite constant, with those of highest amplitude showing the smallest deviation. There is even greater consistency (a lower value for σ/p_m) for the sum of the nine periods (the reciprocal of the fundamental frequency).

It seems quite clear that we have here an harmonic spectrum, not a source-generated modulation. We must now differentiate between a source-generated harmonic spectrum and one arising from a pulsed source coupled to a tracheal resonance. We make the following observations.

A tracheal resonance should give rise to an exponential amplitude decay within the apparent modulating period. This seems not to be present.

For a particular resonance, the wave forms contained within the apparent modulating period should be sinusoidal with a relatively constant period corresponding to the resonant frequency. We see here departure from a sinusoidal form together with "instantaneous" frequency values ranging over an interval greater than 1.5 kc/s.

The mean frequency of the unfiltered signal should correspond to the first resonance frequency of the trachea, and would only by rare coincidence equal the value for a particular harmonic. We have seen that the mean frequency coincides with that of the ninth harmonic.

Ames[11] gives the length of the chickadee trachea as 20 mm; hence the quarter and half wave-length resonances will fall at 4.4 and 8.8 kc/s. The mean frequency is 3.7 kc/s, well below even the quarter wave-length value.

I conclude that the wave form of the black-capped chickadee's call is due to a source-generated harmonic spectrum.

Source-generated Pulses Modulated by a Tracheal Resonance

As indicated earlier, I have not found a completely unambiguous example of this acoustical process in bird song. The closest approach is offered in the buzzy call of the American woodcock (figure 89).

In figure 89, *a* is the oscillogram for the call, *b* the corresponding sonagram, and *c* the harmonic spectrum determined using the wave analyzer. Figure 90 represents a 10-msec fragment which includes a full "modulating" period together with portions of the preceding and following periods. At top is the time-amplitude array; at bottom are plotted "instantaneous frequencies" for successive sinusoids.

The mean modulating period for the entire phrase is 5.80 msec, corresponding to a frequency of 172.5 c/s. The mean of all sinusoidal periods in the entire phrase corresponds to a "carrier" or "resonant" frequency of 4788 c/s.[12] The mean period ob-

---

11. Peter Ames, Museum of Vertebrate Zoology, Univ. of California, Berkeley. Personal communication.
12. Counting the time interval for 100 successive periods is an accurate method for determining mean frequency when the individual periods all have substantial amplitude. When, as here, the amplitude varies over a factor 10–20, results become ambiguous since there is the possibility, even the probability, that very low amplitude periods may be skipped in the counting process.

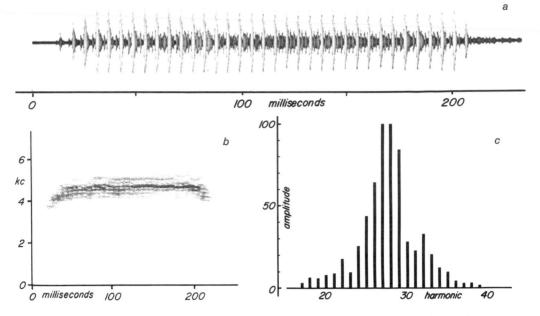

FIGURE 89. American woodcock buzzy call: *a*, the oscillogram; *b*, the sonagram; *c*, the harmonic spectrum.

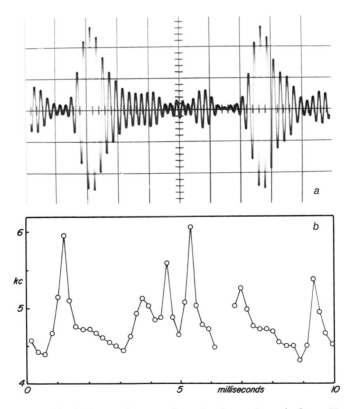

FIGURE 90. A 10-msec fragment from the phrase shown in figure 89:
a, amplitude; *b*, "instantaneous" frequencies.

tained by averaging periods of high amplitude in ten successive modulating periods corresponds to a mean frequency of 4876 c/s; the corresponding mean modulating frequency is 173 c/s. The ratio of the carrier frequency to the modulating frequency for the two sets of measurements are 27.7 and 28.2, respectively. These ratios are not sufficiently precise to permit a positive statement as to whether or not the "carrier" frequency is an integer multiple of the "modulating" frequency.

We note from figure 90 that the high amplitude periods closely approximate a sinusoidal form; also that these periods correspond to a relatively modest frequency variation (less than 500 c/s). While this finding would appear to exclude a source-generated *harmonic spectrum*, the possibility remains that the wave form could be due to a source-generated *modulation* (case II).

In figure 91 I have plotted amplitude and frequency for a single modulating period. On the amplitude envelope stars represent an exponential decay fitted to points at maximum and 50 percent of maximum amplitude. The fit appears reasonable for the high amplitude portion of the modulation; this evidence favors the pulsed source hypothesis.

Fant (1960, p. 240) gives the following formula for determining the band width of the resonance, considered as a filter:

$$B_1 = \frac{\log A_1/A_2}{t_1 \pi \log e}.$$

For the woodcock, the band width according to this formula is 425 c/s, a reasonable value.

In an effort to cast further light on this difficult problem I have isolated the second formant from the vowel "a" as heard in the word "had." Figure 92 shows a single

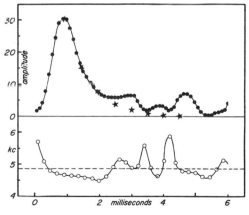

FIGURE 91. American woodcock: A single modulating period. Modulating frequency 173 c/s; mean "carrier" frequency 4880 c/s. The stars show an exponential decay fitted at 100% and 50% amplitude.

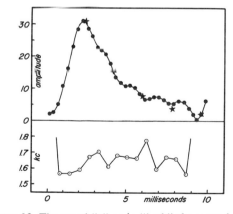

FIGURE 92. The vowel "a" as in "had," the second formant; a single modulating period. Modulating frequency 106 c/s; mean "carrier" frequency 1630 c/s. The stars show an exponential amplitude decay fitted at 100% and 50% amplitude.

repetitive "modulating" period with amplitude and instantaneous frequency plotted as for the American woodcock. Again the stars show a curve of exponential decay fitted to maximum and half-maximum amplitudes. Here the band width from Fant's formula is 125 c/s.

We see the close similarity between the curves in figures 90 and 91; it would be quite easy to conclude that they arise out of the same acoustical phenomenon.

The principal argument against the pulsed source—resonator thesis is provided by the tracheal length, which, for the woodcock is 48 mm.[13]

This length would imply resonance at 1.75 kc/s for a tube closed at one end and open at the other or 3.5 kc/s for a tube open at both ends.

The mean frequency of the woodcock call is 4.8 kc/s, substantially above both resonance values. If, as Ames suspects, the trachea in a living bird is longer than 48 mm the disparity becomes even greater.

The disparity between the resonances associated with a trachea 48 mm long, and the observed values, forces us to discard the pulsed source-resonator hypothesis. There is, on the other hand, nothing to preclude interpreting the woodcock's call as a source-generated modulation.

Finally it may be useful to say a few words about the occurrence of these four acoustical phenomena in bird song.

One sees beat notes occasionally, not frequently, but these are merely a special case in the simultaneous use of the two acoustical sources, discussed in a previous chapter.

Source-generated modulations, on the other hand, are very common; in fact, in whistled song one encounters modulated phrases much more frequently than those which are not modulated. The modulations, as noted earlier, may or may not be repetitive. They do, however, embrace an almost infinite variety (chapter 8).

Source-generated harmonic spectra are also quite common, much more so, however, in what the behaviorists designate as "calls" than in "song." Some birds, e.g., the black-capped chickadee and its European relatives have songs without higher harmonic content. For other bird groups, notably among the nonpasserines, vocalization will be entirely through calls with substantial harmonic content. I shall discuss in greater detail the occurrence of harmonics in songs and calls in a later chapter.

As indicated earlier, I have been unable to find a single clear-cut example of a pulsed source coupled to a tracheal resonance. To say positively that they do not exist would require examination of a very large collection of bird songs, but the fact that no unambiguous example has been found among several hundred songs makes the existence of this acoustical phenomenon at least unlikely.

13. Peter Ames, Museum of Vertebrate Zoology, University of California, Berkeley (private communication), says the trachea in the alcoholic specimen he examined was quite compressed, i.e., in the living bird it might well be longer. Hence the 48 mm. length should be regarded as a minimum value.

Chapter 8   SOURCE-GENERATED MODULATIONS

I have previously defined modulation as the superposition, on a sound of a given amplitude and frequency, of a modifying process which changes amplitude or frequency or both. It is postulated that the unmodulated sound arises in the tympanic membrane, induced to vibrate by air flowing through the constricted syringeal passage, with frequency controlled by tension applied to the membrane through the syringeal musculature. The amplitude will be dependent on the mean cross-sectional area of the syringeal orifice which in turn is the resultant of the pressure in the clavicular sac opposed by the tension applied to the membrane. It is possible that the area of the syringeal orifice may also be influenced through appropriate positioning of the external labium. Modulation will occur when the steady state condition is disturbed due to changing tension in the membrane, changing pressure in the air sac, insertion or withdrawal of the external labium in the syringeal passage, or by a combination of these effects.

Modulated notes and phrases are very common in bird song; in fact they are much more frequently observed than simple unmodulated notes. A glance at the songs illustrated in chapter 4 (figures 20–39) will show the predominance of modulated phrases with only a few, the osprey and the Carolina chickadee for example, comprising a series of unmodulated notes.

The modulations are infinite in their variety. They may be repetitive within a given phrase with modulating frequencies up to 400 c/s; the modulation may stress either frequency or amplitude; the frequency or amplitude envelopes within the modulating period may have almost any form; the modulation itself may change form progressively within a given phrase. Many modulations are not repetitive and may range from simple glissandi to the extraordinary complexity seen within the repetitive phrases of the slate-colored junco or in the song of the tree swallow. Only the very slow modulations can be perceived as such by the human ear; in most cases the modulation is so rapid that our ears perceive it only as an unmodulated note of a a particular quality.

We normally think of quality or timbre of a musical note in terms of an associated harmonic spectrum. It was perhaps quite natural to assume that the easily recognizable differences in quality between phrases making up the songs of birds arise out of the same phenomenon. We find, however, that harmonic spectra are rarely present in whistled song; differences in quality or timbre arise out of the effect on human ears of a modulation in frequency and amplitude too rapid for us to perceive as such.

What a bird hears cannot be said with certainty. There is evidence (Pumphrey, 1961) that temporal discrimination in birds is perhaps ten times more acute than in humans. We can, for example, hear a trill or vibrato as such if the modulation frequency does not exceed about 30 c/s. A bird on the other hand may recognize a modulation whose frequency is 300 c/s or more. Hence it is possible, even probable, that birds perceive their rapid modulations as such, not as notes of varying quality. If so, the information content of a particular song will be greatly increased.

In any event, we must endeavor to explain these highly variable and complex modulations in terms of the available anatomical evidence if we are to produce an acceptable hypothesis for bird vocalization.

I should perhaps pay special tribute here to the song sparrow, whose extraordinary virtuosity has greatly facilitated the preparation of this chapter. Within its singing range of about two octaves the song sparrow produces notes and phrases of unbelievable variety; a single individual may have a richer repertoire than an entire genus of less gifted singers. There is always interpretive uncertainty if one must assemble data from many diverse species; the task is much less difficult if one can compare modulations for a single species. This the song sparrow permits us to do.

Table 3 shows a group of repetitive modulations taken from song sparrow songs (the modulation for bird 2 is shown in detail in figures 85 and 86). Table 4 presents similar data for a number of passerines. Unfortunately the virtuosity of these birds, with the possible exception of Bewick's wren, is considerably less than for the song sparrow; hence I can show only one or two modulations for each species. In both tables modulations have been selected for which the form of the repeating frequency and amplitude envelopes is roughly sinusoidal. In all cases the modulating frequency has the same value, whether it is determined from amplitude or frequency data.

TABLE 3. SONG SPARROWS

Bird*	Modulating Frequency c/s	Carrier Frequency c/s	Excursion from Carrier Frequency Above	Below c/s	Frequency Modulation %	Amplitude Modulation %	Frequency at Amplitude Minima
1a	296	2480	160	340	10.2	38	Low
1b	286	5980	130	120	2.1	17	Low
2	291	3060	210	330	8.8	41	Low
3a	309	3310	620	270	13.4	73	High
3b	278	3400	210	340	8.1	21	Low
4	283	3510	270	340	8.7	17	Low
5	286	3710	100	110	2.8	0	—
6	149	4330	90	250	3.9	47	Low
7	329	4930	440	350	8.0	12	High
8	306	5590	250	400	5.8	19	Low
9	189	6340	270	100	2.9	33	High
10 High Voice	351	5410	1590	560	19.8	75	High
10 Low Voice	351	2870	210	120	5.7	48	High
11 High Voice	372	6860	930	1150	15.1	65	Low
11 Low Voice	370	3620	210	110	4.6	52	High

* Each number represents a different individual; a and b represent phrases in the same song.

TABLE 4

Bird*		Modulating Frequency c/s	Carrier Frequency c/s	Excursion from Carrier Frequency Above	Below c/s	Frequency Modulation %	Amplitude Modulation %	Frequency at Amplitude Minima
Eastern kingbird		156	6330	880	520	11.3	42	High
Traill's flycatcher	a	159	3320	930	470	21.1	53	High
	b	179	3820	860	410	16.6	63	High
Bewick's wren	a	233	3350	150	170	4.8	12	Low
	b	229	3770	180	330	6.7	47	Low
	c	203	2810	110	170	5.0	39	Low
Rock wren		156	3510	330	190	7.3	45	High
Brown thrasher		162	3570	270	470	10.3	42	Low
Varied thrush	a	124	3350	150	80	3.5	45	Low
	b	179	3800	150	50	1.3	22	Low
Townsend's solitaire	a	135	4250	—	—	9.0	64	High
	b	109	2890	180	260	7.5	59	Low
Black-throated blue warbler		232	5350	970	1350	21.6	75	Low
Blue-winged warbler		227	6250	470	1890	18.9	76	Low
Golden-winged warbler		140	8460	1090	500	9.3	58	High
Western meadowlark		184	3070	140	90	3.9	79	High
Redwinged blackbird		120	4960	1640	650	23.1	79	High
Brambling		358	3270	340	270	9.2	12	Low
Lapland longspur		144	3690	250	80	4.4	67	High

* a, b, and c represent phrases in the same song.

Frequency modulation is defined as the mean frequency excursion from the carrier frequency expressed as a percentage of carrier frequency, i.e.,

$$\% \text{ FM} = 100 \left[\frac{F_{max} - F_{min}}{2F_c} \right],$$

where F_{max}, F_{min}, and F_c are maximum, minimum, and carrier frequencies, respectively.

Amplitude modulation is defined as the *difference* between maximum and minimum amplitudes expressed as a percentage of their *sum*, i.e.,

$$\% \text{ AM} = 100 \left[\frac{A_{max} - A_{min}}{A_{max} + A_{min}} \right].$$

We see that in all but one case the amplitude modulation is substantially greater than the frequency modulation.

For the song sparrow modulating frequencies appear to cluster about an upper limit of 300 c/s. It is most unlikely that frequencies of this order can be produced by neural pulses operating one or more times per modulating period; a more probable explanation assumes 300 c/s as the natural frequency of an oscillating system comprising one or more pairs of syringeal muscles, with the mass of the system, the muscular tension, and the elasticity of the muscle tissue controlling the frequency. The few values below 300 c/s may be due to the involvement of a greater mass of muscle tissue. The high values, 350 and 370 c/s, are associated with cases where two voices are being simultaneously modulated, perhaps implying less than twice the mass associated with a modulation applied to only one of the tympaniform membranes.

In table 4 we see a somewhat greater spread in modulating frequency among the various species, ranging from a low of 109 c/s for one of the phrases of Townsend's solitaire, to a high of 358 c/s for the buzzy call of the brambling. It is unfortunate that the available examples for these species are so few; one cannot with certainty speak of a limiting modulating frequency such as the 300 c/s apparently characteristic of the song sparrow.

If these modulations are indeed due to the syringeal muscles oscillating at their natural frequency, one would expect to find modulating frequency increasing with increasing carrier frequency. This is because the carrier frequency produced in the tympanic membrane will increase as the tension in the membrane is increased, and this in turn requires larger forces, hence greater tensions in the syringeal muscles. If, however, the tympanic membranes are very thin (Setterwall, 1901) the forces required to stretch them, so that they will vibrate at higher frequencies, may be quite small and the effect on modulating frequency correspondingly slight.

While the song sparrow data show no relationship between carrier and modulating frequencies, there is at least a hint of such a relationship for the passerines in table 4.

Note examples a and b for Traill's flycatcher, the varied thrush, and Townsend's solitaire. For all three birds modulating and carrier frequencies appear directly related. The situation for Bewick's wren is less clear; the lowest modulating frequency is associated with the lowest carrier frequency, but the other two examples are at best ambiguous.

In both tables we see that carrier frequencies are rarely integer multiples of the modulating frequency, further evidence that these are source-generated modulations.

Note also that amplitude minima may be associated either with frequency maxima or minima, without apparent correlation with carrier frequency. The asymmetry of the frequency excursion appears to be related to this phenomenon; when amplitude and frequency minima occur together the larger frequency excursion is *below* the carrier; when amplitude minima are associated with frequency maxima the larger frequency excursion is *above* the carrier. These relationships provide important evidence for the physiological processes producing these modulations.

Figure 93a shows a single modulating period for Bewick's wren (b in table 4) and figure 93b a modulating period for a song sparrow (3a in table 2). In these figures and in those which follow frequency is the reciprocal of the period for successive sinusoids. Amplitude is the mean of the positive and negative voltages for successive sinusoids scaled from the oscillograms (in some cases, to give more detail, positive and negative voltages are shown separately, both plotted as if they were positive). Open circles are frequency values; filled circles are amplitudes.

In both figures the modulating period is the same, whether derived from frequency or amplitude values. We see also the close coupling of frequency and amplitude. For Bewick's wren the amplitude varies *directly* with the frequency; we call this direct coupling. For the song sparrow the amplitude varies *inversely* with the frequency; we call this inverse coupling.

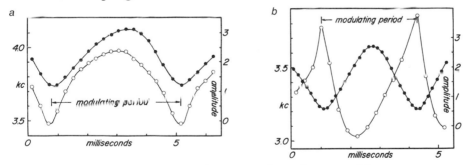

FIGURE 93. Direct and inverse coupling within a modulating period: *a*, Bewick's wren; *b*, song sparrow. Filled circles are amplitudes; open circles, frequency.

Figure 94 shows amplitude/frequency plots for the modulations in figure 93 (*a*, Bewick's wren; *b*, the song sparrow). The open circles indicate rising frequency, the closed circles falling frequency. Both figures show characteristic hysteresis loops.

Figure 95 shows two complex modulations for which amplitude-frequency coupling is direct. Figure 95*a* is a fragment of a phrase from the song of Townsend's solitaire showing three successive modulating periods. This phrase starts without modulation; the modulation begins and intensifies as the phrase proceeds. Note that the amplitude excursion follows closely the increase in frequency excursion. At bottom is a relatively long and complex modulation from the song of Blyth's reed warbler.[14] The close coupling of amplitude and frequency is clearly shown. Figure 96 shows amplitude/frequency plots for these two modulations; we see again the characteristic hysteresis loops.

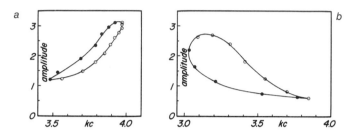

FIGURE 94. Amplitude/frequency plots for the modulations in figure 93: *a*, Bewick's wren; *b*, song sparrow. Open circles are rising frequency; filled circles, falling frequency.

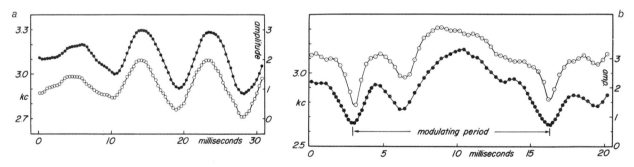

FIGURE 95. Two examples of direct coupling: *a*, Townsend's solitaire; *b*, Blyth's reed warbler. Filled circles are amplitudes; open circles, frequency.

Figure 97 is a modulating period from a phrase sung by a redwinged blackbird. Here the amplitude/frequency coupling is inverse. Figure 98 is an additional example of inverse coupling; figure 98*a*, a modulating period from a repetitive phrase of the slate-colored junco with the corresponding amplitude/frequency plot in figure 98*b*.

In figures 93–98 I have selected cases where the coupling is either direct or inverse for the entire modulation. There are, however, many examples in which the coupling may be of both kinds within a single modulating period. In these cases the coupling is direct *below* a particular frequency; inverse *above* it.

14. Bird recordings from the Swedish Broadcasting Corporation.

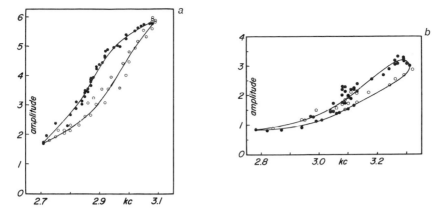

FIGURE 96. Amplitude/frequency plots for the modulation in figure 95: *a*, Town-send's solitaire; *b*, Blyth's reed warbler. Open circles are rising frequency; filled circles, falling frequency.

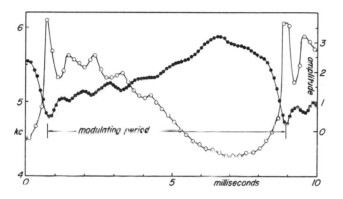

FIGURE 97. Inverse coupling in a modulating period from the song of a redwinged blackbird. Filled circles are amplitudes; open circles, frequency.

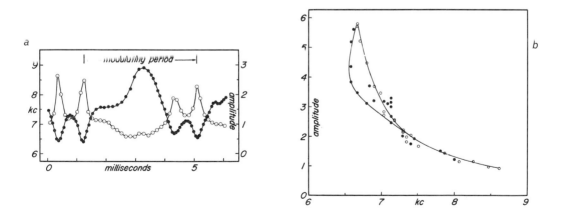

FIGURE 98. Inverse coupling in a modulating period from the song of a slate-colored junco: *a*, time/amplitude and frequency arrays; filled circles are amplitudes; open circles, frequency. *b*, amplitude/frequency plot; open circles are rising frequency; filled circles, falling frequency.

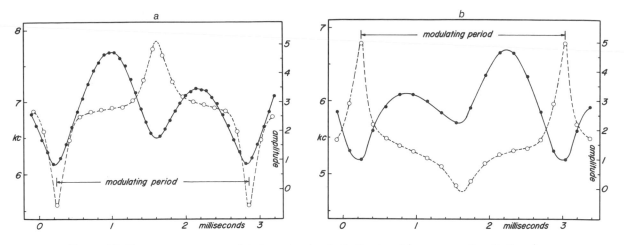

FIGURE 99. Two song sparrow modulations showing both direct and inverse coupling. Both voices were being modulated in these phrases; we show the modulation only for the upper voice. Inversion frequency: *a*, 6.8 kc/s; *b*, 5.4 kc/s. Filled circles are amplitudes; open circles, frequency.

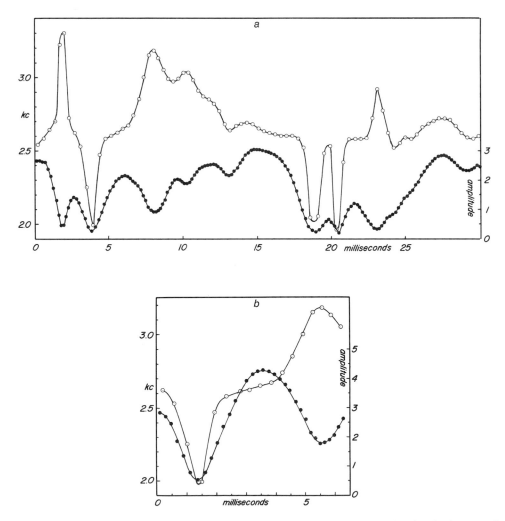

FIGURE 100. A nonrepetitive modulation from the song of a brown thrasher showing both types of coupling: *a*, 30-msec fragment; *b*, small portion of the modulation starting at 3 msec with the time scale expanded. Filled circles are amplitudes; open circles, frequency.

Figures 99a,b show two such modulations, both for song sparrows. Figure 99a is a typical modulating period for the high voice of bird 11 in table 3; figure 99b, the corresponding modulation for bird 10.

In figure 99a we see amplitude directly coupled with frequency up to about 6.8 kc/s, and inversely coupled at frequencies above that value. The inversion value of 6.8 kc/s is also the carrier frequency for the modulation. In figure 99b we see the same phenomenon; direct coupling below about 5.4 kc/s, inverse coupling above that value. Here again the inversion frequency is also the carrier frequency for the modulation.

Figure 100 is a relatively long and complex modulation from the song of a brown thrasher. This modulation is not repetitive, hence we cannot speak of a modulating period; the modulation appears to proceed in a completely random manner. Figure 100a is a 30-msec fragment of the modulation; figure 100b, a small portion beginning at about 3 msec has been expanded to show greater detail. Amplitude/frequency plots for the two fragments are shown in figure 101. The plot for the 6-msec fragment is quite selfconsistent, that for the longer fragment shows considerable scatter. The scatter is to be expected in view of hysteresis effects, and the superposition, on the rapid modulation, of a longer term rise and fall in amplitude. In any event the figures give a reasonable approximation of the form of the amplitude/frequency relationship. Both show the inversion point at about 2.7 kc/s, which is also the mean frequency for the 30-msec fragment.

Figures 102a,b show a modulating period from a song sparrow phrase: a, the entire modulating period, and b, 3-msec fragment (starting at 5 msec). Figure 102c is the amplitude/frequency plot for the entire modulation. Again figure 102c shows considerable scatter, for the reasons given above, but the general form of the relationship is reasonably clear. The inversion point approximates the carrier frequency of 5.9 kc/s.

From the evidence presented above it is clear, at least for rapid modulations, that frequency and amplitude are closely coupled. The coupling is direct (frequency and amplitude rising together) up to a particular frequency; above that frequency the coupling is inverse (amplitude falls as frequency rises). Modulations may occur entirely below the inversion frequency, in which case the coupling will always be direct. There are many examples in which the frequency passes through the inversion point, and both direct and inverse coupling are observed. For these cases the inversion frequency appears always to approximate the mean or carrier frequency of the modulation.

The conclusion seems inevitable that such close coupling of frequency and amplitude must arise from a *single* physiological mechanism, for it is most unlikely that two completely separate physiological processes, one controlling frequency, the other controlling amplitude, could possibly produce such precise coupling.

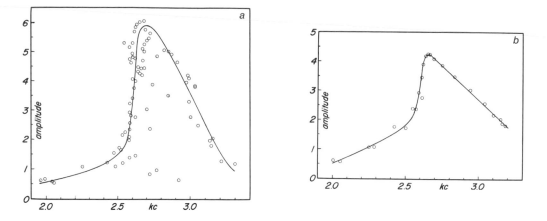

FIGURE 101. Amplitude/frequency plots for the modulation in figure 100. *a*, the 30-msec fragment; *b*, the 8-msec portion.

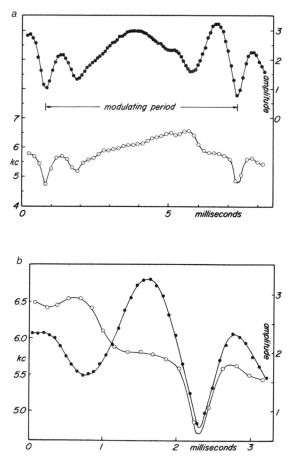

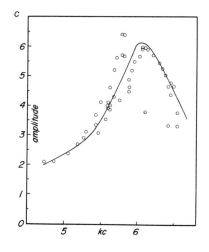

FIGURE 102. A song sparrow modulation showing both direct and inverse coupling: *a*, single modulating period; *b*, fragment starting at 5 msec at an expanded time scale; *c*, amplitude/frequency plot for the modulating period in figure 102*a*. Filled circles are amplitudes; open circles, frequency.

Fortunately we find just such a mechanism in the tympanic membranes, vibrating
in the bronchial lumen, with frequency and amplitude controlled by the associated
syringeal musculature.

Figure 103 is a diagrammatic representation of the syrinx showing a single bronchial passage, with the lungs at left. The tympanic membrane m is bowed inward into
the bronchial lumen by the pressure p in the clavicular air sac. The tension t produced
by the elastic syringeal muscles ms counterbalances the pressure p and produces a
given tension in the membrane. When the tension is sufficient to produce a passage at
d, air will flow[15] and induce vibration in the membranes, at a frequency which will be
a function of the tension in the membrane.

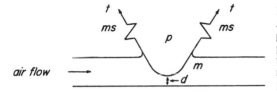

FIGURE 103. A simulation of a single syrinlgea passage.
Air flows from the lungs at left to the trachea at right:
p, the pressure, in the clavicular sac, forces the tympanic membrane m into the bronchial lumen. Tension
t is produced in the membrane by the syringeal
muscles ms. The resultant of the two forces (p and t)
produces the passage d.

If we start with just sufficient tension t to balance the pressure p, d will be zero, and
no air will flow. A small increase in t will open the passage, permit the membrane to
vibrate at a frequency corresponding to t, but the amplitude of vibration will be
restricted to low values by the small value of d. As t increases, frequency and amplitude will increase together, as a larger value for d permits greater vibrational amplitude in the membranes. With further increase in membrane tension, and correspondingly greater values for d, we arrive at a point where the air flow passing through the
syringeal constriction can no longer stimulate the membrane to vibrate through the
allowable distance d, and the amplitude will decrease. At the limit, i.e., a tension
sufficiently great to open the syringeal passage fully, the amplitude will become zero,
and the air flow from the lungs will escape through the trachea without sound
production.

If one had sufficient data on masses of the various parts, the elastic moduli of
membrane and musculature, the pressure p, etc., one could presumably calculate the
form of the amplitude/frequency relationship. Failing such information we must fall
back on the experimental data as shown in the figures. Unfortunately the hysteresis
effects prevent determining the relationship with reasonable precision. Qualitatively,
however, theory and experiment appear in good agreement.

It is, moreover, difficult to see how any of the other recognized anatomical features
of the syrinx could produce these effects. Variations could possibly arise in the clavic-

15. It should be understood that air flow is used here in an acoustical sense, i.e., a time-varying flow controlled by the vibration of the tympanic membrane. There could well be air leakage past the syringeal constriction, but this air flow would be continuous (analogous to a DC, as opposed to an AC component), hence
producing no sound.

ular sac pressure, p, but since the air sacs in the bird's body are interconnected and presumably have considerable volume and mass, it is inconceivable that the pressure could be varied as rapidly as a modulating frequency of 300 c/s would demand.

The true larynx can open and close, perhaps with sufficient rapidity, but a change in the size of the exit orifice so produced would affect amplitude alone, not frequency. Furthermore closure of the laryngeal orifice would equalize the pressure on either side of the tympanic membrane, with loss of the vibrational stimulus due to air flowing through the constricted syringeal passage.

The semilunar membrane can have no effect, since there is no associated musculature to change its position. Even if there were, there would seem no possibility of producing the observed frequency/amplitude coupling.

We come finally to the external labium, a pillow-like process mounted on the bronchial half-ring directly opposite the tympanic membrane. It will be recalled that Setterwall found muscular attachments which in his view could change its shape, perhaps also the degree of its penetration into the bronchial lumen. The external labium certainly has an acoustical role to play, as we shall see shortly, but its motion in and out of the bronchial lumen would change amplitude only, without affecting frequency, even assuming that it could vibrate at rates approaching the observed modulating frequencies.

So far we have considered only those modulations in which frequency and amplitude are coupled. We have explained their occurrence physiologically as the superposition of two oscillating systems, the syringeal musculature on the one hand and the tympanic membrane on the other which, acting together in the syrinx, will produce sounds in which frequency and amplitude are necessarily related. Vibration of the tympanic membranes produces the carrier frequency, oscillation of the syringeal muscles the modulating frequency.

There are, however, many examples in which the amplitude changes without an associated change in frequency. Figure 104 shows an entire modulated phrase (phrase 1a in table 3). We see that modulating and carrier frequencies remain constant during the entire phrase, that the percent frequency modulation is also essentially constant, and that amplitude is coupled (directly in this case) with frequency. There is, however, an overall change in amplitude, which rises from zero through a maximum and falls to zero as the phrase ends. This overall change in amplitude is not associated with a corresponding change in frequency, hence must be due to the operation of a physiological process which is different from those previously considered.

Figure 105 is a long tremolo (barely discernible as such to my ears) produced by a song sparrow (a, the oscillogram, b, the sonagram, and c, amplitude and frequency plots for a single modulation). We see that frequency remains substantially constant in spite of an amplitude modulation approaching 100%. There are small frequency

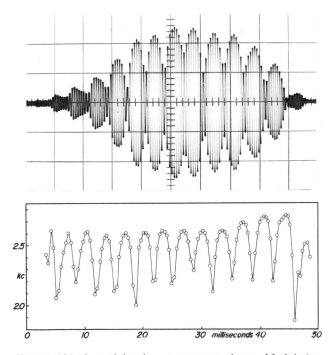

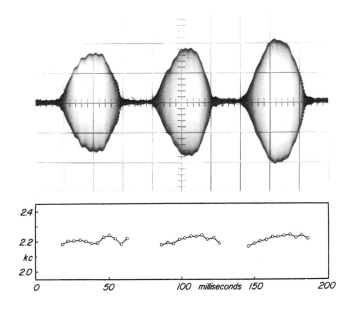

FIGURE 104. A modulated song sparrow phrase. Modulating frequency is relatively constant at 300 c/s, as is the peak of the frequency excursion, 2.6–2.7 kc/s. Note, however, the gradual rise and fall in amplitude from beginning to end of the phrase.

FIGURE 106. Three notes from a song sparrow tremolo with a repetition rate of 17 notes per second. The frequency is held to ± 1.5%, equivalent to one quarter of a musical semitone.

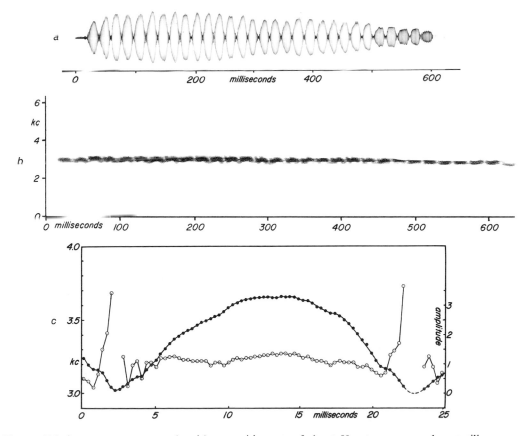

FIGURE 105. A song sparrow tremolo with a repetition rate of about 50 notes per second: *a*, oscillogram; *b*, the corresponding sonagram; *c*, a single note showing time/amplitude (filled circles) and time/frequency (open circles) arrays.

changes at nodes in amplitude but no regular change in frequency as amplitude rises and falls.

Figure 106 shows three notes from another song sparrow tremolo, this one readily perceptible as such to human ears. The repetition rate is 17 notes per second. The frequency within each note and from note to note is remarkably constant, the deviation from the mean amounting to only 1.5% (about 1/4 of a musical semitone). Here again is a case of simple amplitude modulation.

It is also apparent in figure 75 that the amplitude of unmodulated notes, for the song sparrow, is independent of frequency throughout the bird's singing range. In figures 76–79, there is no significant change in amplitude during glissandi in which frequency changes by at least a factor of two.

Finally, in those song sparrow modulations for which amplitude and frequency show both direct and inverse coupling, we have inversion frequencies at 5.4, 5.9, and 6.8 kc/s. This observation also would appear to demand some additional process which changes amplitude without associated changes in frequency.

We find the necessary control mechanism in the external labium whose movement within the bronchial lumen provides a simple method for controlling amplitude without affecting the tension, hence the frequency, produced in the tympaniform membrane.

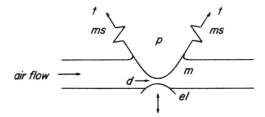

FIGURE 107. The external labium el whose associated musculature controls its penetration into the bronchial lumen, thus producing a change in the area of passage d without an associated change in frequency. (See figure 103 for abbreviations.)

In Figure 107 we have redrawn figure 103, depicting the external labium (*el*) as a bulge in the bronchial wall directly below the tympaniform membrane. If we assume that the labium can "follow" or "retreat" from the membrane, as it moves through the bronchial lumen, we see that amplitude may be varied without frequency change, to produce notes or phrases in which only amplitude modulation is encountered.

As noted earlier, amplitude modulation without frequency modulation is relatively uncommon; hence it is difficult to find data from which one can derive the time constant associated with movement of the external labium. For the tremolo in figure 105 the modulating frequency is about 50 c/s, much lower than the 300 c/s associated with coupled modulation. In figure 108, however, we see that "labial" modulation can be quite rapid (*a*, oscillogram of the entire phrase (a song sparrow fragment); *b*, the corresponding sonagram; and *c*, a single short note (the third in the phrase) with frequency and amplitude plotted together).

The short note comprises two parts whose total duration is about 3.5 msec. Except at nodes in amplitude, frequency changes relatively little; hence one can appropriately assume a modulation due almost entirely to labial movement. This has a very short time constant since in the first part of the note the amplitude rises and falls in a little over 2 msec, implying a modulating frequency approaching 500 c/s.

In summary, it would appear that the rapid modulations, so frequently encountered in bird song, are of a kind in which frequency and amplitude are coupled. Amplitude modulation per se, produced by movement of the external labium, seems to be used in longer notes and phrases to produce relatively slow changes in amplitude. The single example in figure 108, however, would appear to show that labial modulation can inherently be quite rapid, and the relative scarcity of rapid modulations involving amplitude alone may be a matter of choice, not of necessity.

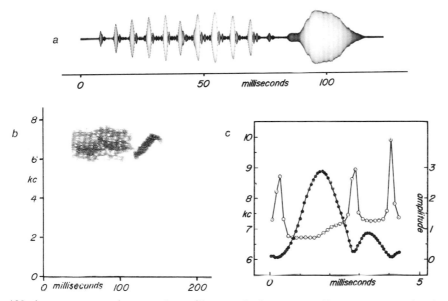

FIGURE 108. A song sparrow phrase: a, the oscillogram; b, the corresponding sonagram; c, time/amplitude (filled circles) and time/frequency (open circles) arrays for the third short note (at about 30 msec on the oscillogram).

There are some birds, whose syringeal equipment does not include an external labium. For these species we would expect a much more limited singing range since acoustical efficiency would be possible over only a small frequency interval. This may be the situation for such species as the common loon, the western grebe, the Laysan albatross, the osprey, etc. (chapter 4) whose singing ranges appear to embrace only a few hundred cycles per second.

We present now a "portfolio of modulations" to give some indication of their variety, and to show also that most birds make use of this device in their songs.

Figure 109 is the song of the little tinamou.[16] This is a whistled song (harmonics

16. Recorded by Rodman Ward in Trinidad, in February 1965.

are absent) and embraces a rather small frequency interval; a bit more than a musical whole tone. We see, however, large and rapid amplitude modulations in portions of the song, without substantial changes in frequency.

Beebe (1925) has examined in detail the syrinx of a related species, the variegated tinamou, and believes that vocalization is produced by air flowing through an orifice between two pillow-like processes on either side of a bronchial passage. His description is reminiscent of the pursed lips with which our whistle is produced.

Figures 110 and 111 show the "pumping" song of the American bittern. I was stimulated to an analysis of this song by Forbush's (1925) delightful discussion of its characteristics. Forbush says among other things that the American bittern's song is sometimes heard as a "pumping" song; at other times as a "stake driving" song. He found that one's impression of the song depended upon the direction from which it was heard, and whether or not the bird was facing the listener. The figures present at least a clue as to the reason for the difference. Figure 110a shows an oscillogram of the entire song, figure 110b an oscillogram of the low frequency components, and figure 110c the frequencies for the unfiltered song. The low frequency components produce the pure "pumping" song. The high frequency portion superimposed on the second phrase produces the "stake driving" effect. If then the position of the listener is such as to reduce the amplitude of the low frequency components "stake driving" is emphasized. The converse situation would emphasize "pumping." The second phrase is shown in greater detail in figure 44. Figure 111 is a small fragment of the first phrase. We see the low frequency component at 200 c/s, and superimposed upon it a very short, low amplitude glissando extending from about 2.0 to 3.5 kc/s. I cannot say whether or not this surprisingly high note contributes to the "stake driving" effect.

The bittern does not produce modulation in the precise sense we have been discussing. The succession of notes comprising its song, their form and duration show how an appropriate arrangement of essentially musical notes can produce for our ears a nonmusical effect.

Figure 112 is the song of the sage grouse. The first two phrases, at frequencies between 350 and 600 c/s, show no remarkable features. The third phrase begins conventionally, then at 250 msec the second voice chimes in with almost explosive violence, rising and falling in a double glissando extending over two octaves. The final phrase shows a similarly rapid rise in amplitude. This perhaps explains the function of the large inflatable air sacs on the neck of the grouse. A sudden release of the compressed air in the sacs could well account for the nearly instantaneous "attack" in phrases three and four.

Figures 113a and b show the whole song and a repetitive phrase, from the little nightjar.[17] While the individual notes are modulated, the interest, as for the bittern,

---

17. Paul Schwartz, "Bird Songs from the Tropics" (a collection of records).

arises out of the effect of the notes, their spacing and amplitude envelopes, on the listener. The phrase sounds much like the tinkling of small bells.

Figures 114 and 115 are for the "be" phrase from the song of the Eastern phoebe. Figures 114a,b show oscillogram and sonagram, respectively, for the entire phrase; figure 115 a single modulating period taken at about 400 msec. We see that frequency/amplitude coupling is largely direct, with a small amount of inverse coupling at about 5.0 kc/s.

Figure 116 is a short phrase from the song of a tree swallow. The modulation comprises a succession of deep glissandi sung by the two voices in sequence. Voice 1 extends from 0–25 msec, voice 2 from 25–35 msec, voice 1 again from 30–80 msec, and voice 2 from 70 msec to the end.

Figures 117 and 118, Bewick's wren illustrate a change in modulation in midphrase. Figures 117a,b are the oscillogram and sonagram for the entire phrase; figure 118 shows typical modulating periods (time/amplitude and time/frequency arrays) from the two parts of the phrase. In figure 118a coupling is inverse (amplitude rising as frequency falls); in figure 118b there appears to be inverse coupling at the beginning of the modulation, but one must infer labial movement (amplitude dropping without change in frequency) as the modulation ends.

Figure 119 is a single modulating period of the upper voice in the terminal phrase of a wood thrush. The entire phrase is shown in figure 53. Here the coupling is inverse, with amplitude rising as frequency falls. Note also the complexity of the amplitude and frequency envelopes. If only one syringeal muscle were involved, the envelope of the modulation should be roughly sinusoidal. The complexity here may arise out of the involvement of several syringeal muscles operating in different phase relationships.

Figure 120 is a single repetitive phrase from the terminal portion of the song of a blue-winged warbler. The phrase comprises four distinct subphrases embracing a frequency range of nearly a full octave (4.5 to 8 kc/s). Figure 121 shows time/amplitude/frequency arrays for the second and third subphrases. In subphrase 2 (frequency above 6 kc/s) the amplitude/frequency coupling is inverse, whereas in subphrase 3 (below 6 kc/s) the coupling is direct.

Figure 122 shows two phrases from the song of a Tennessee warbler. Both phrases are glissandi; and in figure 122b, the glissando embraces nearly two octaves. There are no clear-cut amplitude/frequency relationships and one must assume labial modulation to maintain amplitude at a reasonable level over so large a frequency interval. Glissandi covering substantial frequency intervals appear characteristic of the songs of many of the wood warblers (Parulidae). (For a few additional examples, see figures 76, 77, 78.)

Figure 123 is a repetitive phrase from the song of the blackpoll warbler. The entire phrase, in fact the entire song, is above 8.5 kc/s and extends briefly to 10.6

kc/s. To my fairly ancient ears the song at high amplitude sounds like a series of short hisses without musical content. The figure shows two subphrases each with fairly complex modulation. The glissandi on a linear frequency scale appear to embrace a considerable range, but the entire interval within the song is actually somewhat less than four musical semitones.

Figure 124 is a repetitive phrase from the song of a vesper sparrow. This could be characterized as an "interrupted" glissando. (The filled circles are frequencies determined from the sum of ten successive sinusoidal periods; the open circles are from successive single sinusoids.) Note that during the "interruption," an interval of about 5 msec, the frequency/amplitude coupling is inverse. For the *whole* phrase, there is no clear-cut relationship and we must assume that labial modulation is involved. The glissando embraces a full octave.

In figure 125 we show a single repetitive phrase from the song of a slate-colored junco. The repetition rate is 11 per second and the phrase is repeated many times without significant alteration. Note the extreme complexity of the phrase (not perceived by human ears) and that the bird's two voices are used alternately in producing the three subphrases. Figure 125*a* is the whole phrase, lasting about 70 msec; figure 125*b* is the central 25-msec section, which shows the overlapping characteristic of the use of both acoustical sources. The phrase embraces a full octave; there are no clear-cut frequency/amplitude relationships.

In figure 126 we show a repetitive phrase from the song of a swamp sparrow. The repetition rate is 5½ per second and, as is the case for the junco, the phrase is repeated many times without alteration. Note the extraordinarily rapid glissando in subphrase 2. Here differences between *successive* periods are equivalent to instantaneous frequency changes approaching 500 c/s. The entire phrase embraces nearly two full octaves; again there are no clearly defined amplitude/frequency relationships.

In figures 127 and 128 we show two complex phrases from the songs of two song sparrows. In both figures the oscillograms (*a*) and sonagrams (*b*) for the whole phrase are shown, respectively, as well as a single modulating period (*c*).

In both phrases coupling is both direct and inverse with an inversion point approximating the carrier frequency. Both modulating periods are longer than those given in table 3. In figure 127*c* the modulating period is 11.5 msec, corresponding to a modulating frequency of 87.5 c/s. In figure 128*c* the modulating period is 6.1 msec, corresponding to a modulating frequency of 163 c/s. Here, as for the wood thrush (figure 119) we assume the involvement of two or more syringeal muscles, operating out of phase with each other, to account for the long modulating period and the complexity of the amplitude and frequency envelopes.

The phrase in figure 128 has an extra feature in that both acoustical sources are used. Voice 1 is responsible for the short glissando which begins the phrase; voice 2 is responsible for the complex modulation, which starts just before the glissando ends.

Figure 129 is a song sparrow phrase in which the modulation is not oscillatory but comprises a series of subphrases differing widely in their amplitude and frequency envelopes. The phrase is remarkable in embracing the entire frequency range of the song sparrow, viz., the two full octaves from just over 2 to 8.5 kc/s, all within an interval of 200 msec. In addition, subphrase two, at 50 msec, begins with both voices in operation, each producing a short glissando.

Figure 130 is a phrase from the song of a Lapland longspur. In this phrase both acoustical sources are used, and each is separately modulated. Source 1 begins the phrase at 4.2 kc/s, and is followed after a 20-msec interval by source 2 beginning with a glissando at 5.3 kc/s. Source 1 is silent from 80 to 110 msec, then drops down to a sustained note of low but constant amplitude. This note has a harmonic at 5.8 kc/s (not shown as a separate oscillogram). Meanwhile source 2 performs a long diminuendo at about 4.8 kc/s and produces finally a crescendo at 5.5 kc/s. Note the curious short peak in frequency at 150 msec occurring in source 2 and in both harmonics of source 1.

I have reserved the best, or perhaps I should say the most remarkable series of modulations for the end of this collection. Figure 131 shows two phrases from the song of the brown-headed cowbird. This undistinguished bird, of unprepossessing appearance and habits, is the undisputed winner in the decathlon of avian vocalization. The whole song, from which these two fragments were taken, is shown in figure 35. Peterson (1947, p. 216) characterizes it as "bubbly and creaky, glug-glug-gleeee." There are in fact two "gleeees," and the phrases in figure 131 are, respectively, the second "glug" and the first "gleeee." Consider now the following features.

1. The frequency range in the two phrases is, by a large margin, wider than in any other song. The range extends from 0.75 to 10.7 kc/s, nearly four octaves!

2. The maximum frequency at 10.7 kc/s is higher than we have found for any other bird, just "nosing out" the 10.6 kc/s at the top of the blackpoll warbler song.

3. Both voices are used in the second subphrase of the "glug," and the frequency spread between the two voices, two full octaves, is exceeded only by that of the American bittern.

4. The first note in the "gleeee" is the shortest I have encountered. It lasts a bit less than 2 msec and comprises a "packet" of 12 sinusoids at 6.4 kc/s.

5. The glissando at 50 msec in the "gleeee" is one of the most rapid, covering the range 5–8 kc/s in 4 msec and 23 sinusoids—an average of 130 c/s per sinusoid.

6. The modulating frequency in the high voice in subphrase 2 of the "glug" is higher by a large margin than any other, about 700 c/s. The song sparrow, for example, rarely exceeds 300 c/s as a modulating frequency.

The brown-headed cowbird's performance is truly remarkable. What useful purpose is served by a "glug" comprising five widely different subphrases, and a "gleeee" containing a note of negligible duration, two rapid glissandi, and a peak frequency of 10.7 kc/s, only madam cowbird will know.

We have seen that modulation in bird song may take a variety of forms, some of very great complexity. It is a surprising fact that birds appear able to repeat these modulations, song after song, or phrase after phrase, with extraordinary precision. As a single example, figure 132 shows a song sparrow phrase as it appears in six successive songs.

The bird is 11 in table 3, and a single modulating period for the high-pitched voice is shown in figure 99a. The bird is modulating both voices simultaneously (and at the same modulating frequency) in a phrase whose duration is about 100 msec. The carrier frequency of the upper voice is 6.8 kc/s, that of the lower 3.6 kc/s. At the end of the modulation the lower voice rises in a rapid glissando (itself modulated) and ends the phrase at a sustained frequency of 5.5 kc/s.

In making the six oscillograms in figure 132, the sharply cutting filters were set successively to pass frequencies first above, then below a fixed value of 6.0 kc/s. The same setting was used for the phrase as it appeared in the six successive songs; in each case the amplitude of the sustained terminal note was set at a given value. The figures show both voices, with the high-pitched voice at the top.

Note the precision with which both voices repeat, not only the modulation itself but the relative amplitudes of the two modulations. The terminal notes differ somewhat but not significantly in their amplitude envelopes, but the duration of the entire phrase and of the phrases arising from the two voices is quite constant.

It seems most unlikely that a phrase of this complexity, with such a high modulating frequency (370 c/s), and with both voices sounding simultaneously, can be entirely innate. Some form of learning process must be involved so that the bird need only signal the appropriate "code" for the entire phrase to be reproduced.

The ability of birds to repeat complex phrases with great precision suggests that a quantitative appraisal of deviations from the mean might give some worthwhile clues as to their temporal perception or resolving power. I examine this question, as well as the ability of birds to resolve frequency differences, in the next chapter.

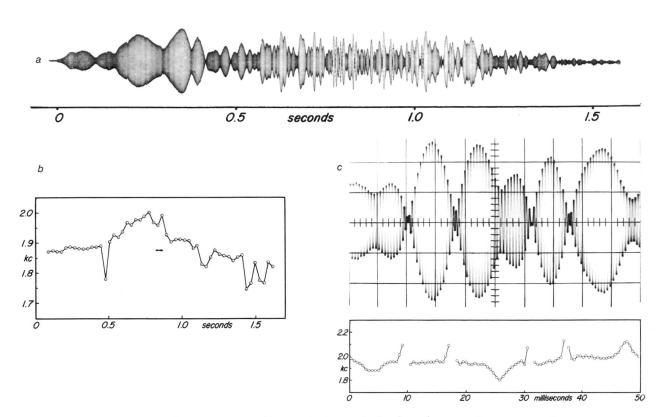

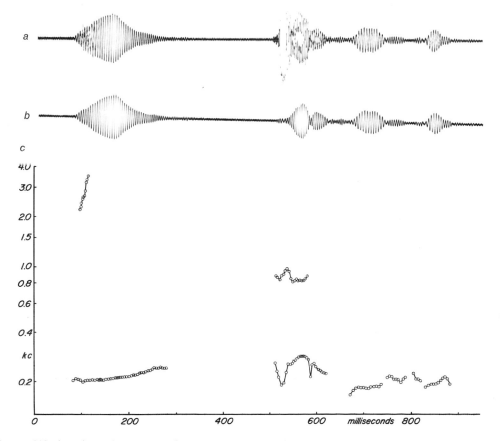

FIGURE 109. Little tinamou: *a*, the oscillogram; *b*, frequencies for the entire song taken at 30-msec intervals from the mean of 100 successive periods; *c*, 50-msec fragment starting at 0.8 sec showing amplitude and frequency (from successive sinusoids).

FIGURE 110. American bittern "pumping" song. Two oscillograms for the entire song: *a*, without filtration, and *b*, with filters set to embrace the interval 100 to 500 c/s; *c*, frequencies from successive sinusoids.

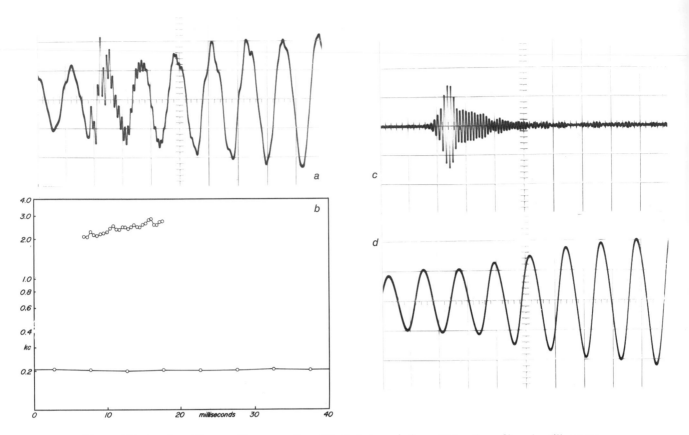

FIGURE 111. American bittern, a 40 msec portion of the first phrase in figure 110: *a*, the unfiltered oscillogram; *b*, the corresponding frequencies from successive sinusoids; *c*, *d*, oscillograms for the two voices, isolated by filtration.

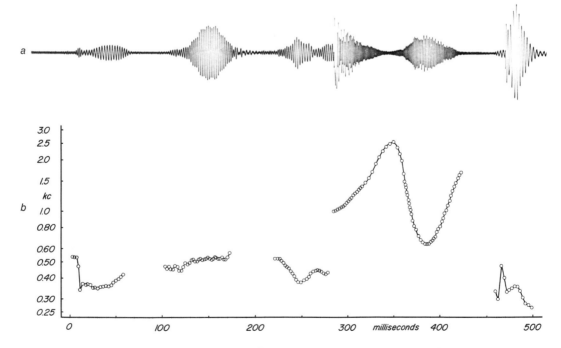

FIGURE 112. The song of the sage grouse: *a*, the unfiltered oscillogram; *b*, the corresponding frequencies. The frequency scale is logarithmic, to give proper weight to the low frequency values.

122

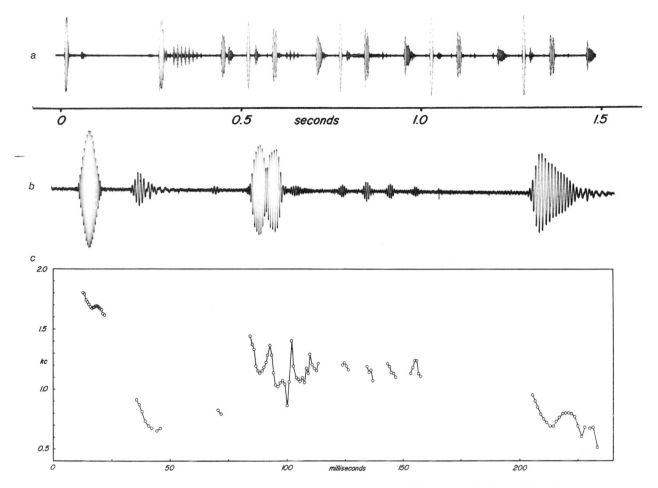

FIGURE 113. Little nightjar: *a*, oscillogram for the entire song; *b*, repetitive phrase (the interval 0.5 to 0.75 sec) on an expanded time scale; *c*, frequencies for successive sinusoids.

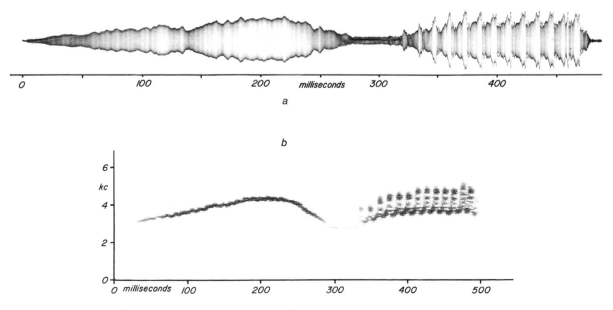

FIGURE 114. Eastern phoebe: *a*, oscillogram and, *b*, sonagram for the "be" phrase.

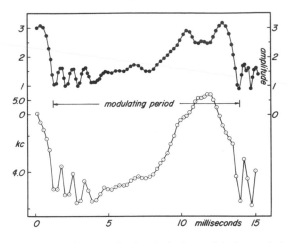

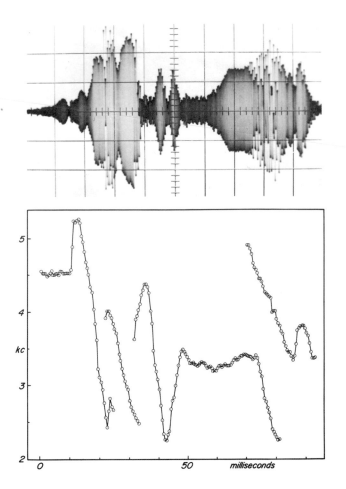

FIGURE 115. Eastern phoebe. A single modulating period starting at about 400 msec in figure 114. For most of the period amplitude and frequency are directly coupled. Coupling appears to be inverse above about 5.0 kc/s. Filled circles are amplitudes; open circles, frequency.

FIGURE 116. Tree swallow. A single phrase showing steep glissandi sung sequentially by the two voices.

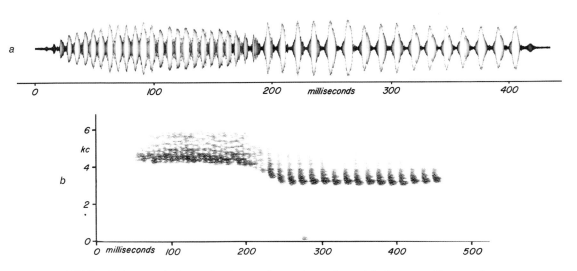

FIGURE 117. Bewick's wren. A phrase showing an abrupt change in modulation: *a*, oscillogram; *b*, sonagram·

124

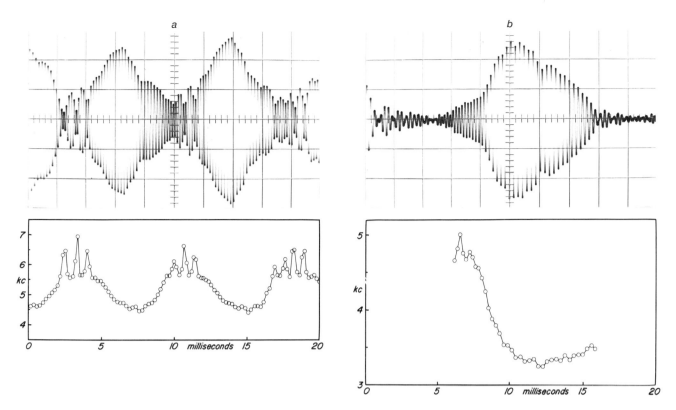

FIGURE 118. Bewick's wren. Modulating periods from the phrase shown in figure 117: *a*, two periods starting at about 150 msec; *b*, single period starting at about 350 msec.

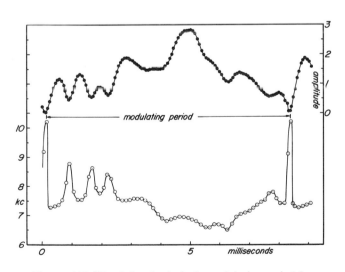

FIGURE 119. Wood thrush. A single modulating period from the high voice in a two-voiced terminal phrase. Filled circles are amplitudes; open circles, frequency.

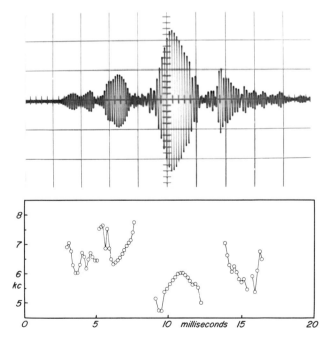

FIGURE 120. Blue-winged warbler. A single phrase from the terminal buzz. Note the four distinct subphrases.

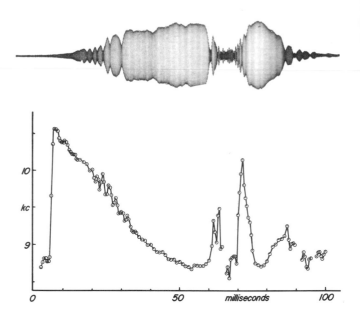

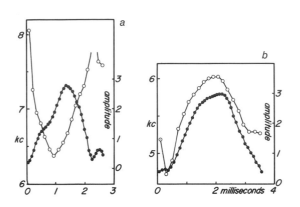

FIGURE 121. Blue-winged warbler. Subphrases 2 and 3 from figure 120: *a*, coupling for subphrase 2 is inverse; *b*, direct for subphrase 3. Filled circles are amplitudes; open circles, frequency.

FIGURE 123. A repetitive phrase from the song of the blackpoll warbler. The song begins at low amplitude and rises in a crescendo to the central portion, then diminishes in amplitude as the song ends.

FIGURE 122. Tennessee warbler: *a*, *b*, two phrases from the same song. In the second phrase the glissando embraces nearly two octaves.

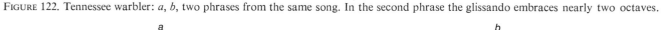

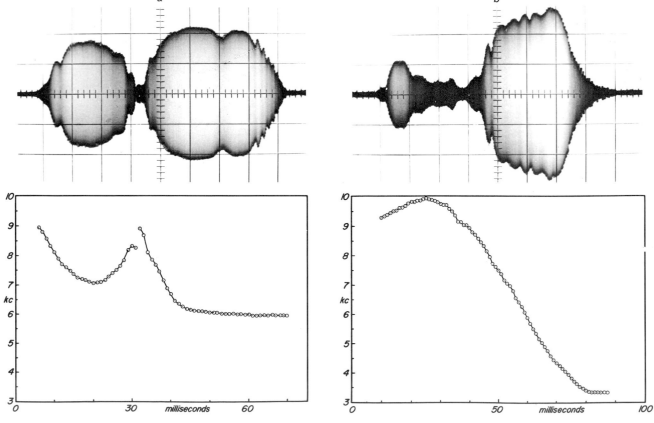

126

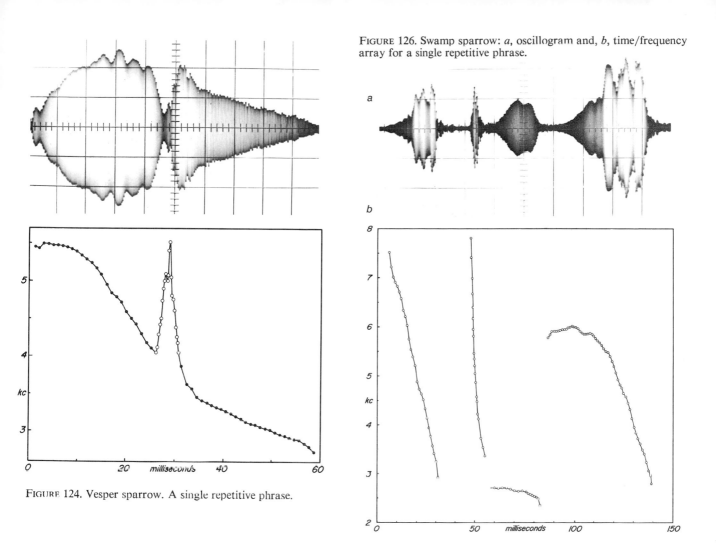

FIGURE 126. Swamp sparrow: *a*, oscillogram and, *b*, time/frequency array for a single repetitive phrase.

FIGURE 124. Vesper sparrow. A single repetitive phrase.

FIGURE 125. Slate-colored junco: *a*, single repetitive phrase with frequencies determined from the time interval for 10 successive sinusoids; *b*, 25-msec portion starting at about 50 msec of *a*. Frequencies are for single successive sinusoids.

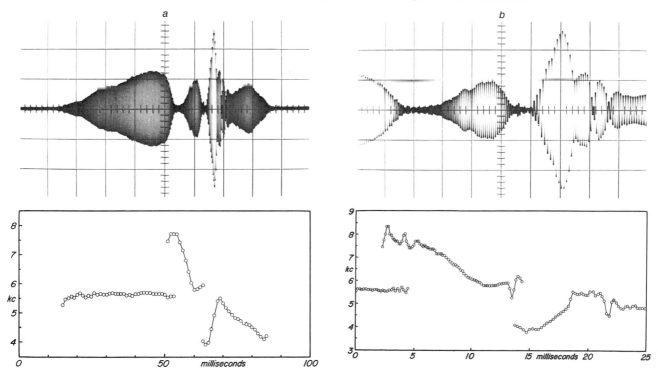

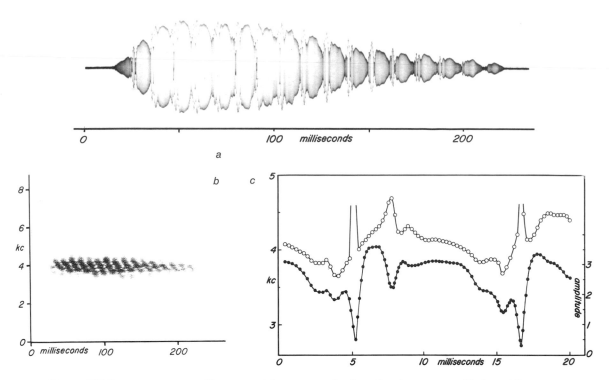

FIGURE 127. Song sparrow: *a*, oscillogram and, *b*, sonagram for the entire phrase; *c*, amplitude and frequency arrays for a single modulating period. The modulating period extends from 5 to about 16.5 msec corresponding to a modulating frequency of 87.5 c/s. The carrier frequency is 4.14 kc/s. Filled circles are amplitudes; open circles, frequency.

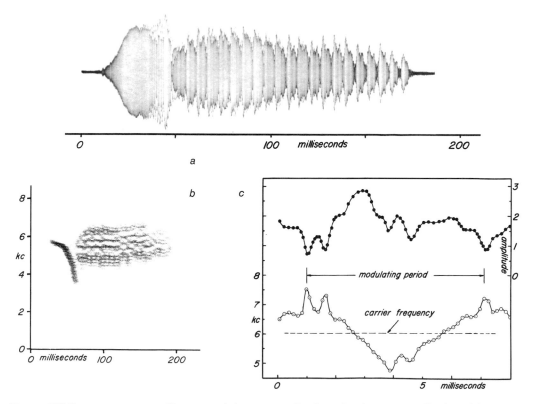

FIGURE 128. Song sparrow: *a*, oscillogram and, *b*, sonagram for the entire phrase; *c*, amplitude and frequency arrays for a single modulating period. The modulating frequency is 163 c/s, the carrier frequency 6.03 kc/s. Filled circles are amplitudes, open circles, frequency.

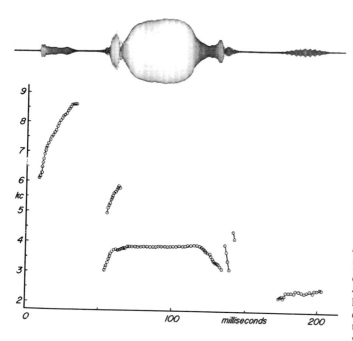

left

FIGURE 129. A song sparrow phrase. The frequency range in this short phrase (about two octaves) includes the maximum and minimum frequencies found in all song sparrow songs.

below

FIGURE 130. A Lapland longspur phrase. Three oscillograms: *a*, unfiltered; *b*, the frequency interval 4.5 to 5.6 kc/s; *c*, the frequency interval 2.5 to 4.5 kc/s. Oscillogram for the harmonic of the low frequency phrase is not shown. *d*, Frequencies determined from the time interval for 10 successive sinusoidal periods.

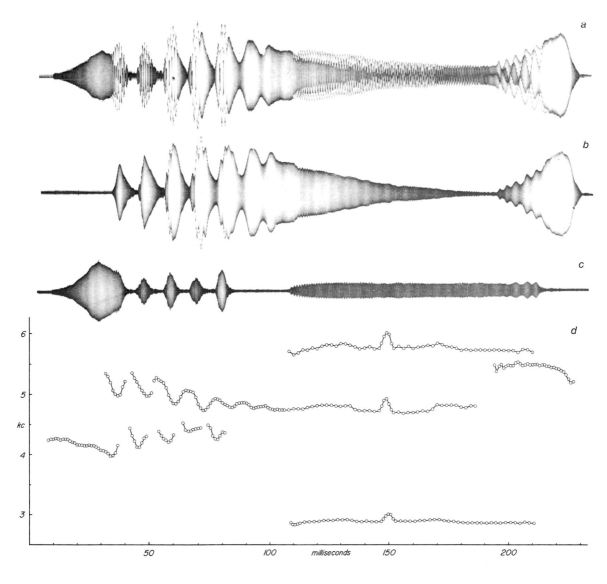

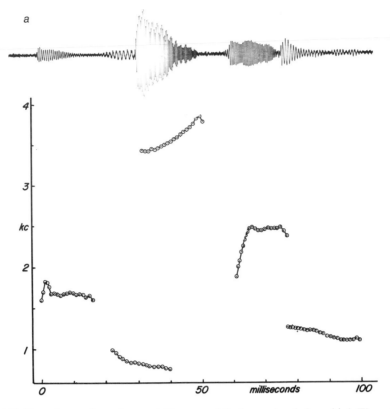

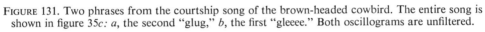

FIGURE 131. Two phrases from the courtship song of the brown-headed cowbird. The entire song is shown in figure 35c: *a*, the second "glug," *b*, the first "gleeee." Both oscillograms are unfiltered.

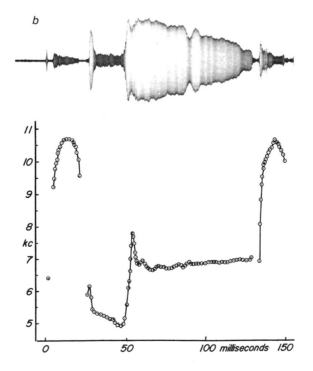

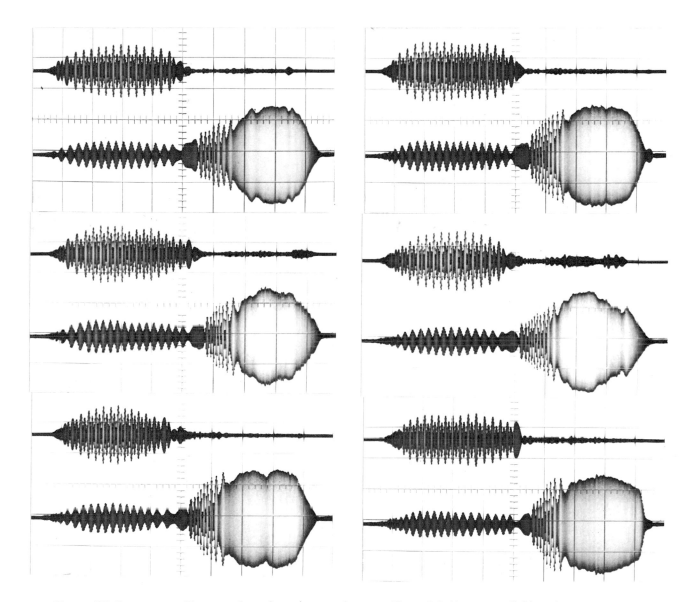

FIGURE 132. Song sparrow. The same phrase from six successive songs. The scale is 11 msec per division; the phrase is 100 msec long. Filters were set to pass signals first above, then below 6.0 kc/s; the corresponding oscillograms were photographed on the same film, with appropriate vertical scale movement to separate the two arrays. The six pictures are for successive songs for the same bird. Amplitude was adjusted to a fixed value for the terminal portion of the lower voice.

Chapter 9　FREQUENCY AND TIME PERCEPTION

We have seen in the previous chapter that rapid modulation, in frequency, in amplitude, or in both, appears to be a characteristic feature in bird song. The modulations may be oscillatory in character with modulating frequencies up to 300–400 c/s. In such cases frequency and amplitude appear to be coupled, and the coupling may be direct, inverse, or of both kinds within a single phrase. Or the modulation may be random with a series of notes of varying duration and with widely differing frequency and amplitude envelopes combined to produce a complex phrase which may or may not be repetitive.

While the characteristics of these rapid modulations provide strong evidence as to the *physiological* processes involved in bird vocalization, their *behavioral* significance is more difficult to appraise. It is impossible for the human ear to resolve these modulations, either as to pitch or frequency, and they sound to us like single notes of varying quality or timbre. The significant factor, however, is the response of the avian ear, and the question is of vital importance in a behavioral sense, since the quantitative ability of the bird to resolve differences in frequency and time bear directly on the information content of the song, hence on the ability of the bird to communicate with his kind.

The literature is not very helpful in defining avian resolving power either as to frequency or time. We attempt in this chapter to develop for both parameters such evidence as may be taken from the songs themselves. It is recognized that these can give no more than a measure of the bird's *performance*, viz., constancy of intonation within a phrase, or constancy of a given time interval within a series of repetitive phrases. If, however, it can be shown that an aural feedback exists through

132

which the stimulus to the avian ear is transmitted to the syringeal musculature, one can assume with some confidence that *performance* and the ability to *discriminate* are indeed related. Konishi's experiments with deafened birds provide strong evidence for such a mechanism.

In one series of experiments Konishi (1964) deafened nestlings of the Oregon junco at ages 47–90 days after hatching, and before the onset of subsong. The birds were kept in acoustical isolation. The song of the wild Oregon junco comprises a series of identical phrases repeated 10 to 20 times. The deafened birds sang songs with repetitive phrases, and within the same frequency range as their wild relatives, but were unable to maintain the identity of successive phrases, which varied randomly and over wide limits. Since wild birds maintained identity of successive phrases with great precision, the evidence would appear compelling that this behavior is in fact due to an aural feedback, lost in the deafening process.

Konishi (1965) obtained similar results with deafened white-crowned sparrows; he stated (op. cit., p. 772), in part, that

> . . . it is reasonable to conclude that however the pattern of a song heard during the critical period is stored in the central nervous system, auditory feed back is indispensable for its reproduction in the corresponding vocal pattern. In other words, the bird must hear its own sound in order to reproduce what it has heard and remembered from some months previously.

Aside from Konishi's experiments there are other indications that avian *performance* is indeed related to the ability to *discriminate*. Were this not the case, one would have to assume that bird songs are innate, not learned, and many examples can be adduced to show that such an hypothesis is at least unlikely. Consider, for example, the mockingbird with its extraordinary virtuosity and its ability to produce convincing imitations of many other birds, or the song sparrow with its considerable repertoire of complex songs none of which appears even remotely related to those of its neighbors. Finally, there is good evidence that the young of certain species of gulls can distinguish the cries of their parents even when many other adults in the colony are calling simultaneously. Surely this finding implies learning on the part of the young and a corresponding ability to discriminate.

Frequency Discrimination

For frequency perception in birds the experiments of Sigrid Knecht (1940), who used a conditioning technique, are most frequently cited. Her work on frequency discrimination was done with only two individuals, a budgerigar and a crossbill. She concludes for these two individuals that frequency discrimination is as good or better than it is for humans. As shown in table 5, this conclusion is not supported by her data (*op cit.*, pp. 191–196).

TABLE 5

Bird	*Knecht*			*Human**$*$
	f c/s	Δf c/s	Δf/f × 10³	Δf/f × 10³
Budgerigar	650	5	8	4.0
Budgerigar	2600	24–36	9–14	2.0
Budgerigar	10400	1100–2000	110–190	3.3
Crossbill	10400	1100	110	3.3

* Shower and Biddulph (1931). The figures are for 40 db above threshold.

If we compare the Δf/f values for Miss Knecht's birds with those for humans, we see that the human ear is twice as sensitive at 650 c/s, 5–7 times as sensitive at 2600 c/s, and 30 times as sensitive at 10 kc/s. However, the uncertainties inherent in the conditioning technique, and the fact that only two individuals were used casts some doubt on the validity of her results.

To provide additional evidence I have determined frequency deviations within a phrase of relatively constant frequency, selected from the songs of several species.

I turned first to the obliging song sparrow and to a bird for which we have five successive, substantially identical songs.[18] In three of the songs there were six; in two, seven introductory phrases. Each phrase consisted of two subphrases, the first of which contained a steep glissando; the second of about 60-msec duration was held at relatively constant frequency. Figure 133 shows a typical introductory phrase of which the second subphrase, at about 5.5 kc/s, was taken for investigation. Filters were set to isolate this subphrase and frequency was determined from the time interval for 10 successive sinusoids. Frequencies were taken at 2-msec intervals throughout the phrase, giving 30 readings for each phrase. The precision in frequency was ±3–4 c/s.

In Figure 134a we have plotted frequencies as determined for three phrases in three songs. The small open circles, the filled circles, and the large open circles are, respectively, songs 1, 3, and 5. The plots as one goes from left to right are for phrases 1, 3, and 5. With the exception of phrase 5 in song 5 (an anomalous result, as we shall see later), the scatter of the individual frequencies appears to be random for each phrase. Mean frequencies for all 32 phrases are plotted in figure 134b. The drop in frequency from phrase 1 through phrase 7 is real and probably intentional. The interval, amounting to about 300 c/s, is equivalent to a musical semitone.

The standard deviation, σ, was derived for each of the 32 phrases and divided by the mean frequency. The results are shown in figure 135 and table 6. In figure 135, the dashed lines represent the value Δf/f for human perception as determined by

18. Cornell Laboratory of Ornithology, Cut 1.

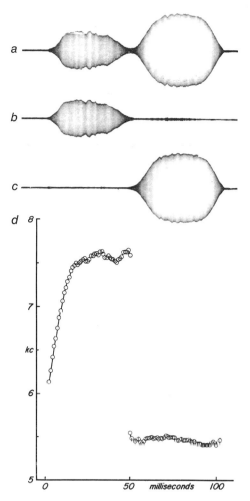

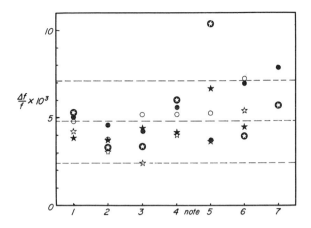

FIGURE 135. Constancy of intonation ($\Delta f/f$) for the 32 introductory song sparrow notes; each symbol represents a particular song. The dashed lines are frequency perception for the human ear at 5.5 kc/s multiplied by one, two, and three.

FIGURE 133. A typical introductory phrase for the song sparrow in Cornell catalog cut one: *a*, unfiltered oscillogram; *b, c*, the two subphrases isolated by filtration; *d*, the corresponding frequencies. The second subphrase (*c*) was used in determining constancy of intonation.

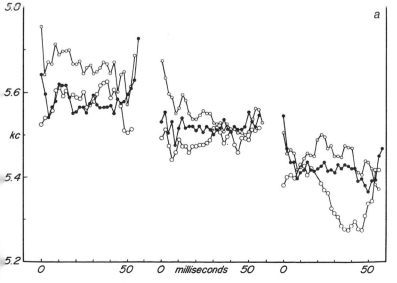

FIGURE 134. Song sparrow: *a*, Frequencies for notes 1, 3, and 5 in songs 1, 3, and 5; each symbol represents a particular song. Frequencies were taken at 2-msec intervals. *b*, Mean frequencies for all notes in five songs; each symbol represents a particular song. The interval 5450 to 5750 c/s is a musical semitone.

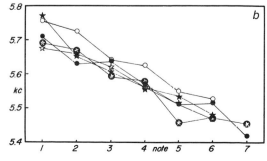

Shower and Biddulph (1931) for 5.5 kc/s, and at twice and three times that value; the anomalous position of note 5 in song 5 is clearly seen.

TABLE 6

	$\sigma/f_m \times 10^3$				
Song	1	2	3	4	5
Note 1	4.77	5.03	4.22	3.84	5.33
2	3.74	4.56	3.06	3.65	3.27
3	5.18	4.21	2.42	4.37	3.34
4	5.18	5.57	4.03	4.18	6.02
5	5.26	3.69	3.67	6.68	10.38
6	7.23	6.91	5.41	4.51	3.96
7		7.84			5.68

Shower and Biddulph give $\Delta f/f \times 10^3$ as 2.4 for human ears at 5.5 kc/s.

The pooled coefficient of variation ($\overline{V}$) for all 32 determinations is 4.91×10^{-3}. This is far better than an interpolation of Miss Knecht's data would lead one to expect, and not far removed from the human ability to discriminate frequency differences.

This song sparrow also seems able to produce a given frequency with considerable precision from song to song, in spite of a relatively long interval between successive songs. Thus the value of $\overline{V}$ for constancy of intonation ($\Delta f/f$) *within* the 32 notes is 4.9×10^{-3}; the value of $\overline{V}$ for the mean frequency of the same note in successive songs is 9.2×10^{-3}. These data suggest that the bird maintains intonation within a phrase to plus or minus one-twelfth of a musical semitone and that it can produce de novo a note at a given frequency to plus or minus one-sixth of a semitone. Perfect pitch for humans is a rarity; it appears to be an integral part of the avian vocal equipment.

We have determined constancy of intonation for a few additional notes sung by several species. The results are shown in table 7.

TABLE 7

Bird	c/s			Human*
	fm	σ	$\sigma/f_m \times 10^3$	$\Delta f/f \times 10^3$
Common loon	902	2.7	2.9	3.0
Varied thrush	2955	6.4	2.2	2.1
Wood thrush	2152	6.7	3.1	1.9
	2526	8.9	3.5	2.0
	3007	13.6	4.5	2.1
	3643	11.2	3.1	2.2
Carolina chickadee	3751	15.7	4.2	2.2
Song sparrow	2225	8.9	4.0	1.9
	2984	19.1	6.4	2.1
	4116	19.5	4.7	2.3
	7885	21.3	2.7	2.9

* Values for human ears as given by Shower and Biddulph at 40 db above threshold.

The long notes in the song of Harris' sparrow permit a somewhat more detailed analysis of constancy of intonation. Figure 136 shows the oscillogram and the corresponding frequencies (open circles) for the first note of a typical song.[19] The duration of the note is 1.3 sec; it begins with a glissando from 3900 to 3560 c/s—presumably intentional—after which the frequency wanders, seemingly at random, over an interval of 40 c/s for about 1 sec. The constancy of intonation ($\Delta f/f$) for this interval (the line connecting the two stars on the figure) is 3.2×10^{-3}; the perception for human ears at this frequency (the dashed line) is 2.2×10^{-3}. The filled circles represent $\Delta f/f$ over 50-msec intervals at selected points in the note; the average value is very close to that for human ears.

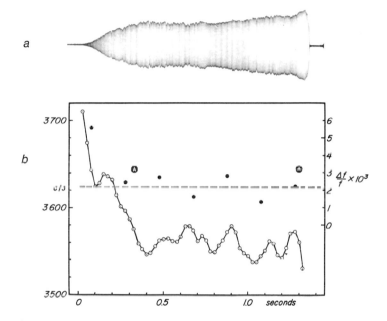

FIGURE 136. Harris' sparrow. The first note: *a*, the oscillogram; *b*, frequencies at an accuracy + 1 c/s (open circles). The line between stars is $\Delta f/f$ for that interval (about 1 sec). The filled circles are $\Delta f/f$ for 50-msec intervals. The dashed line is the value of $\Delta f/f$ for human ears from Shower and Biddulph (1931).

These data would appear to indicate that constancy of intonation during a particular note for these birds is at best equal to, at worst three times, the human ability to perceive frequency differences. On the assumption that perception and performance are related, it would follow that *frequency perception* for the bird could not be worse than these figures for *constancy of intonation*, and could well be substantially better. We cannot tell how hard the bird is trying, in precisely the same sense that we cannot say that a violinist in playing a selection is maintaining intonation as well as he could if he made the necessary effort.

19. Frequencies were calculated from the time interval for 100 successive sinusoids, resulting in a precision for the frequency values of ±1 c/s.

On this last point we have some data. Small (*in* Seashore, 1938, p. 204) measured constancy of intonation, as related to the well-tempered scale, for two violinists playing Schubert's "Ave Maria." We have calculated standard deviations for his data; the results are shown in table 8.

TABLE 8

Violinist	c/s			
	fm	σ	$\sigma/f_m \times 10^3$	$\Delta f/f \times 10^3$*
Slatkin	578	5.0	8.6	4.5
Small	578	5.8	10.0	4.5

* Shower and Biddulph values for 580 c/s at 40 db above threshold.

We see that constancy of intonation for the violinists was about half as good as the ability of the human ear to perceive frequency differences. (I suspect they would have done considerably better when tuning their instruments.) The factor 2 for the violinists, if applied to our avian performers, would suggest frequency perception for birds just about equal to that for humans.

We conclude, then, that constancy of intonation for birds is about half as good as the human ability to perceive frequency differences. Frequency perception for birds, as contrasted with constancy of intonation, may well be as good as for human ears.

Time Discrimination

The literature on time discrimination for birds is somewhat more helpful than that which discusses frequency discrimination. Nonetheless, the conclusions hitherto put forward are far from quantitative. Pumphrey (1961, p. 83) points to Griffin's data on echo location for the oilbird, which when flying in the dark utters a stream of short pulses at a mean frequency of 7 kc/s, with a high repetition rate, and a silent interval between pulses of only 2–3 msec. To discriminate echo delays within the short silent interval manifestly requires a speed of response very much higher than that of which the human ear is capable.

Time discrimination in the human ear has been given by Joos (1948) as approximately 50 msec. He derives the constant in several different ways. Perhaps the most significant is the observation that human speech begins to lose intelligibility at speeds of about 20 phones per second, no matter how loud or clear, or how familiar the dialect. The time discrimination of the oilbird appears to be one or more orders of magnitude better.

Pumphrey also refers to Thorpe's (1959) experiments with chaffinches raised in acoustical isolation. When these birds produced their first song, it was found to be of an extremely simple and restricted type. When placed with adults, singing their normal song, it was found that the hand-reared birds rapidly learned the adult song in all its complexity. The adult chaffinch song, it might be added, contains modulations at least as complex as any shown in the previous chapter. Pumphrey assumes that these modulations would be perceptible to the human ear only if they were slowed to one-tenth normal speed.

From these data he concludes (p. 85) that "the cochlea of a bird is designed to have a speed of response about ten times as high as that of the human ear."

In an attempt to define the temporal resolving power of birds with greater precision I have turned again to an analysis of the songs themselves. Songs were selected in which a given non-oscillatory phrase is repeated many times, and in which the repetitive phrase has easily recognizable features permitting them to be fixed on the time axis with a precision of ±0.1 msec.

Figure 137 is from the song of the grasshopper warbler.[20] In its song the bird repeats this phrase ad nauseam; to our ears it sounds more or less like an unduly prolonged buzz. The oscillogram shows the phrase to be quite complex, comprising three subphrases, the first beginning at 0 msec; the second, a very low amplitude, very short click at about 20 msec; and the third at 25 msec. The features selected for measurement were A, the beginning of subphrase 1; B, the second amplitude maximum (at about 8 msec) of subphrase 1; C, the beginning of subphrase 2; and D, the amplitude peak of subphrase 3. The times at which these features occurred were measured for about 20 successive phrases to a precision ±0.1 msec.

From these time measurements the intervals ΔA, ΔB, ΔC, ΔD were determined, as well as the intervals A-B, B-C, C-D. Mean values for the intervals, together with the standard deviation σ, were calculated from the 20 values. The results are shown in table 9.

TABLE 9. Grasshopper Warbler

Interval		Milliseconds	
		Duration	σ
ΔA		38.55	0.55
ΔB		38.30	0.16
ΔC		38.49	0.43
ΔD		38.45	0.43
	Mean	38.49	0.29*
A-B		7.56	0.32
B-C		12.76	0.22
C-D		4.96	0.14

* ΔA, ΔB, ΔC, ΔD give the interval between phrases, i.e., the reciprocal of the repetition rate. Standard deviations for this interval are considerably higher than those for the intervals *within* the sung phrase. This may imply a deliberate pattern of variation in the repetition rate, and this pattern (when it exists) can be eliminated by statistical procedures which produce a residual deviation for the purely random variation in the repetition interval. The standard deviation so computed (0.29 msec) is much closer to the deviations within the sung phrase.

20. Witherby's "Sound Guide to British Birds," Part 2 (a collection of records).

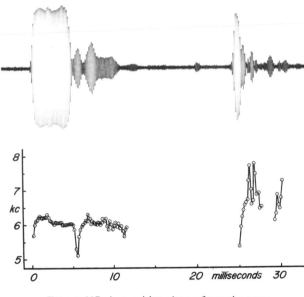

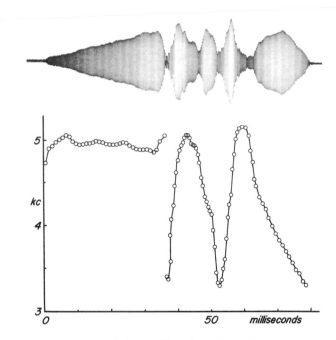

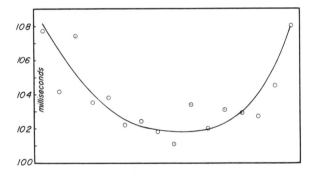

FIGURE 137. A repetitive phrase from the song of a grasshopper warbler.

FIGURE 138. A repetitive phrase from the song of a white-winged junco.

FIGURE 139. The interval between phrases for the white-winged junco in figure 138 from the beginning (left) to the end (right) of the song.

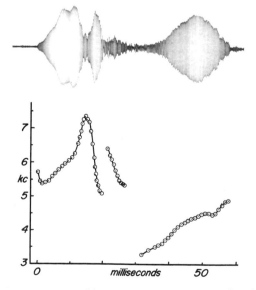

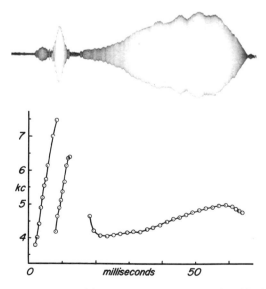

FIGURE 140. A repetitive phrase from the song of a slate-colored junco. The points taken for an analysis (table 11) were A, the beginning of the sung phrase (at zero msec); B, the second amplitude maximum (at 7 msec); and C, the end of the sung phrase (at 64 msec).

FIGURE 141. A repetitive phrase from the song of a chipping sparrow. The points taken for an analysis (table 11) were A, the beginning of the sung phrase (at zero msec); B, the first amplitude minimum (at 15 msec); and C, the end of the sung phrase (at 58 msec).

140

The standard deviations are extremely small (the pooled variation is 0.25 msec) and imply a truly remarkable precision on the time axis. The standard deviation appears to be independent of the time interval, a result to be expected if we are really measuring resolving power.

Figure 138 is a phrase from the song of the white-winged junco. In this particular song the phrase was repeated 17 times with an interval between phrases of about 100 msec. The features selected for analysis were A, the beginning of the phrase (at 0 msec); B, the beginning of subphrase 2 (at 37.5 msec); C, the frequency minimum (53 msec); and D, the end of the phrase (81 msec).

TABLE 10. White-winged Junco

| | Milliseconds | |
Interval	Duration	σ
(Between 1	103.8	2.15
phrases) 2	103.8	0.64*
A-B	37.3	0.64
B-C	15.5	0.54
C-D	28.2	0.80
A-D	81.0	0.79

* In this song there appears to be a pattern, probably intentional, for the interval between phrases (figure 139). Statistical procedures were used to derive a residual, purely random deviation for the repetition rate which is given as the second value in the table. This value is much more consistent with the intervals between features within the song. Determination of the end of the sung phrase was relatively more uncertain than for the other features, probably accounting for the higher values of σ when point D is involved.

For the white-winged junco, temporal precision is poorer than for the grasshopper warbler but the mean value, about 0.6 msec, is nonetheless extraordinarily good.

Figure 141 is a repetitive phrase for the chipping sparrow; figure 140, a similar phrase for the slate-colored junco. The features taken for analysis are indicated in the figure captions; the results are given in table 11.

TABLE 11

| | Chipping Sparrow Milliseconds | | Slate-colored Junco Milliseconds | |
Interval	Duration	σ	Duration	σ
(Between 1	80.6	1.03	82.2	1.45
phrases) 2*	80.6	0.57	82.2	0.27
A-B	14.4	0.42	7.1	0.26
B-C	43.4	0.72	56.3	0.49
A-C	57.8	0.66	63.4	0.50

* As before, statistical procedures were used to derive the purely random variation in the intervals between phrases.

Finally, the repetition interval was determined for 60 successive phrases sung by Savi's warbler. The mean interval was 22.9 msec, and the standard deviation 0.20

msec. There was no significant pattern for the repetition interval within the 60 phrases, hence the measured value of σ was the same as the residual random value.

For the five species σ, the standard deviation for a particular time interval, varied from 0.15 to 0.80 msec; the mean value (the pooled standard deviation) for all intervals in the five phrases was 0.48 msec. This average is certainly higher than the true value, because of the difficulties inherent in measuring the position of the several features on the time axis with the necessary precision. I conclude that temporal discrimination for these small birds is no greater than 0.5 msec, and may well be considerably less. The estimate given by Joos for temporal resolution in the human ear is 100 times greater than this value. The values for birds and humans were, however, based on quite different criteria, and it is entirely possible that the difference underestimates the resolving ability of the human ear. Nonetheless the factor 10 estimated by Pumphrey must surely be low; the data presented here would support a ratio more nearly 50–100 if we can assume precision and perception on the time axis to be synonymous.

It should perhaps be said that comparison between birds and humans as to their relative abilities to perceive frequency and temporal differences is not particularly pertinent. I have discussed perception on this basis simply because this is what has been done in the principal references in the literature.

The absolute values are, however, significant since these define the "information content" in a particular song or call as an avian auditor will perceive it. On this basis frequency discrimination ($\Delta f/f \times 10^3$) for the avian ear lies between 2 and 5, and time discrimination would appear to be no greater than 0.5 msec.

There is then the strong presumption that birds hear *as such* the rapid modulations so characteristic of their songs, and that the information content even in relatively simple songs must be enormous. One readily understands how birds of the same species may recognize individuals from subtleties in their song which are imperceptible to a human listener.

Chapter 10   HARMONICS

We turn now to harmonics as they occur in bird song, in contrast to the whistled phrases without significant harmonic content, which have been discussed in previous chapters.

It would be pleasant if one could enunciate broad generalizations as to the presence or absence of harmonics in the songs of the several bird families. Unfortunately, no statement can be made, even for a single family, which does not have important exceptions. It is fair to say, for example, that in the songs of the Passeriformes phrases in which harmonics appear are relatively rare; that in the nonpasserine birds, phrases with substantial harmonic content are relatively common.

Consider, however, the Corvidae, all of whose North American members have calls rich in harmonics. Among the Paridae the black-capped chickadee has a whistled song, but its scold, after two introductory whistled notes, comprises phrases in which the ninth harmonic predominates. In the Sittidae, the white- and red-breasted nuthatches produce harmonic spectra in their calls, whereas the pygmy nuthatch does not. Among the Mimidae, the mockingbird, the catbird, and the brown thrasher appear to mingle whistled phrases and phrases containing harmonics, almost at random. Among the Sylviidae, the song of the blue-gray gnatcatcher is rich in harmonics; that of the ruby-crowned kinglet contains only whistled phrases. The Parulidae appear to produce only whistled songs, yet even here there is a single exception—the yellow-breasted chat, which is as likely as not to produce calls with harmonic content. Among the Fringillidae, phrases containing harmonics are uncommon. Yet in the song of the common redpoll whistled notes are rare, and phrases are frequently encountered in which the two voices sound simultaneously, each producing its own harmonic spectrum. Even the song sparrow occasionally sings phrases at the low end of its range in which the second and even the third harmonics appear.

The nonpasserine families produce an equally formidable list of exceptions. The tinamous, for example, have whistled songs; among loons and grebes, Gaviidae and Colymbidae, some songs are whistled, some are not. The calls of swans, geese and ducks, Anatidae, almost invariably have rich harmonic spectra; yet some of the tree ducks (Dendrocygninae) produce only whistled songs, and such species as the common teal and the European widgeon produce some sounds which are whistled and some with more or less harmonic content. The hawks, Accipitridae, show great variety in their songs. Many of them, the golden eagle, the osprey, Cooper's hawk, for example, produce whistled songs; others sing phrases in which the second or third harmonic predominates. Shorebirds (Charadriidae, Scolopacidae), owls (Tyronidae, Strigidae), and woodpeckers (Picidae), show equal variability; individual species may produce whistled phrases, other species calls with substantial harmonic content.

And so it goes, with only the following crude approach to a generalization: For *all* birds, whistled phrases are much more common than those with harmonic content; for the Passeriformes as a whole phrases with harmonic content are rare; for the more primitive families a rough approximation would equate phrases with harmonic spectra to those which are whistled.

We must, then, take harmonics as we find them and attempt to fit their occurrence into the physiological and acoustical models which have been developed in previous chapters.

First, in order to demonstrate the premise that whistled phrases have, indeed, an insignificant harmonic content, I present table 12, a random selection taken to show representatives of a number of families, and a substantial range in frequency. The sample is admittedly minute, but additional evidence can readily be obtained from the host of properly taken[21] sonagrams in the abundant literature on bird song, in which many phrases show no perceptible energy at frequencies above the fundamental.

The amplitudes for harmonics 2 and 3 taken with the wave analyzer are higher than the true values, for bird song recordings almost invariably contain extraneous noise which would produce readings on the wave analyzer at any frequency. Further-

---

21. I use the qualification "properly taken" advisedly since it is easy to overload the electronic circuits in the sound spectrograph to the point where spurious harmonics appear on the spectrogram. An example of such overloading appears as figure 2; there are many others in the literature.

more, the process of recording and copying, through distortion in the amplifiers employed, will introduce spurious harmonics.[22]

TABLE 12

Bird	Frequency c/s	Relative Harmonic Amplitudes[1]	
		2	3
Spruce grouse	90	0.7	1.5
Blue grouse	175	1.2	1.6
American bittern	205	5.6	0.5
Great gray owl	225	1.3	1.0
Mourning dove	500	0.9	2.6
Turtle dove[2]	625	3.7	0.7
Screech owl	800	1.0	1.2
Pied-billed grebe	850	1.7	11.0
Wood thrush	1700	3.0	2.1
Human whistle[3]	1800	1.0	0.5
Osprey	1825	8.0	4.0
Gray hawk	2275	3.6	5.8
Wood thrush	2300	1.4	2.8
Yellow-breasted chat	2350	5.5	2.7
Gray jay	2450	2.0	1.9
Purple finch	3000	1.2	0.2
Nightingale[2]	3100	1.9	1.0
Wood thrush	3150	2.0	5.7
Tufted titmouse	3300	2.1	0.6
Western meadowlark	4200	4.3	0.9
Prairie warbler	4800	3.2	1.0
Song sparrow	2300–5600	0.7–2.5	0.1–1.1

[1] The amplitude of the fundamental is taken to be 100.
[2] From British records; all others from master tape for Eastern and Western Field Guide records.
[3] Author whistling directly into microphone.

The Determination of Harmonic Spectra

I have used three methods for determining harmonic amplitudes.

1. If the fundamental frequency is sufficiently high (a considerable frequency separation between successive harmonics) and if frequency changes little during the phrase being analyzed, one can separate harmonics using the sharply cutting filters and measure harmonic amplitudes directly from the resulting oscillograms. Unfortunately this ideal situation rarely obtains.

2. The Hewlett-Packard wave analyzer can be used (as previously described) to measure the harmonic spectra with considerable precision even though a particular harmonic may have an amplitude only a few percent of that of the one

22. A harmonic-free signal generated by a Hewlett-Packard oscillator at 2000 c/s was recorded on a Nagra III-b tape recorder and the harmonic content of the resulting tape analyzed. With the recording volume at zero db on the Nagra VU meter, amplitudes of 0.2 and 1.5 were found for harmonics 2 and 3, relative to an arbitrary value of 100 for the fundamental.

which is dominant. The wave analyzer has a band pass of 45 c/s; hence it will integrate amplitudes over a 20-msec interval. When the frequency of the particular phrase is changing slowly, the integrating process is not disadvantageous. When, however, the phrase is short, or the fundamental frequency is changing rapidly, the method becomes unreliable. Wave analyzer results are also difficult to interpret when the fundamental is low, viz., below about 200 c/s.

3. A photograph is taken of the repetitive wave form on the oscilloscope, from which time-amplitude coordinates are derived. The data are fed to a computer, programmed to produce the coefficients of the corresponding Fourier transform. This method is ideal for steep glissandi or for very short phrases. A small ambiguity arises out of the assumption that the wave form repeats indefinitely, but for our purposes this limitation is not serious. The computer prints out calculated amplitudes, for ready comparison with the original data. If the resulting Fourier series contains a sufficient number of terms, the agreement is excellent.

For cases permitting the use of all three methods, the agreement is good.

A survey of the occurrence of harmonic spectra in bird song shows clearly that for a given species there is a threshold frequency below which harmonics occur, above which one has a whistled phrase without significant harmonic content. This threshold varies widely for different species, from a value near 4000 c/s for the blue-gray gnatcatcher to below 500 c/s for the barred owl. Table 13 illustrates the frequency dependence of the generation of harmonics for a few widely diverse species.

TABLE 13

Bird	Frequency c/s	Relative Harmonic Amplitudes		
		1	2	3
Common loon	650	100	23	3.1
	900	100	1.3	2.9
Barred owl	260	7.5	100	41
	530	100	1.5	6.5
Red-necked grebe	1100	51	100	2.7
	1700	100	1.4	
Catbird	2100	51	100	4.6
	3300	100	0.9	
Hawk owl	1220	100	87	56
	3200–4500	100	negligible	
Dunlin	1400	26	100	71
	3200	100	negligible	

Data such as are presented here are obtainable only when a bird sings over a range of frequencies which embrace the threshold frequency. This circumstance is uncommon since the majority of the Passeriformes sing *only* in the frequency range giving rise to harmonic-free phrases, whereas in other families the converse is true. As we shall see, when we consider the physiological mechanism responsible for harmonic generation, it can safely be said that the harmonic threshold exists for virtually all birds. Whether or not they pass above or below the threshold in their songs or calls appears to be a matter of choice; there is no physiological reason, for example, which would prevent a crow from singing a whistled phrase, or a wood warbler, by way of contrast, singing a phrase with substantial harmonic content.

For a precise determination of the value of the threshold frequency, one must find a bird obliging enough to sing a glissando which passes through that threshold. Birds are not ordinarily so accommodating, but diligent search has uncovered a sufficient number of examples to show how harmonic spectra develop as the fundamental frequency descends below the threshold value.

Figure 142 is a phrase from the song of the versatile song sparrow. It is, as we see, a glissando which begins at 2.0 and ends at 2.8 kc/s. The fundamental and the second harmonic have been separated by filtration and the corresponding oscillograms are shown directly above the frequency plot. The development of the second harmonic lags somewhat behind the start of the phrase; its amplitude builds rapidly to a value several times that of the fundamental, then diminishes as the fundamental frequency rises, and disappears completely between 2.2 and 2.3 kc/s.

In Figure 143, I have plotted relative amplitudes of the first and second harmonics against fundamental frequency, for the song sparrow phrase in figure 142. Note the very small frequency interval, about 200 c/s, embraced in the transition from fundamental to second harmonic. The threshold frequency, defined as the frequency at which adjacent harmonics have equal amplitudes, occurs at 2.15 kc/s.

Figure 144 shows a phrase from the song of a brown thrasher (*a*, the unfiltered oscillogram *b*, the fundamental frequency). One sees in the oscillogram the transitions between first and second harmonics as the fundamental frequency rises and falls, and the disappearance of the second harmonic at about 1.6 kc/s. Figure 145 is a plot of relative harmonic amplitude against fundamental frequency. We see again the sharpness of the transitions; at 1.50 kc/s for harmonics one and two, at 0.78 kc/s for harmonics 2 and 3.

Figure 146 shows harmonic amplitudes and fundamental frequencies for a short phrase from the song of a blue-gray gnatcatcher. Here the transition frequencies are quite high; 3.7 kc/s for the first and second harmonics, 2.2 kc/s for harmonics 2 and 3. Again we see the small frequency interval embraced in each transition.

I can only applaud the good will of the smooth-billed ani in being obliging enough to sing a glissando embracing nearly three octaves (from 485 to 3500 c/s) in which dominance shifts as frequency rises from harmonic 4, through harmonics 3 and 2, to the fundamental. Figure 147 shows the unfiltered oscillogram together with the corresponding fundamental frequencies, and Figure 148 the relative amplitudes for

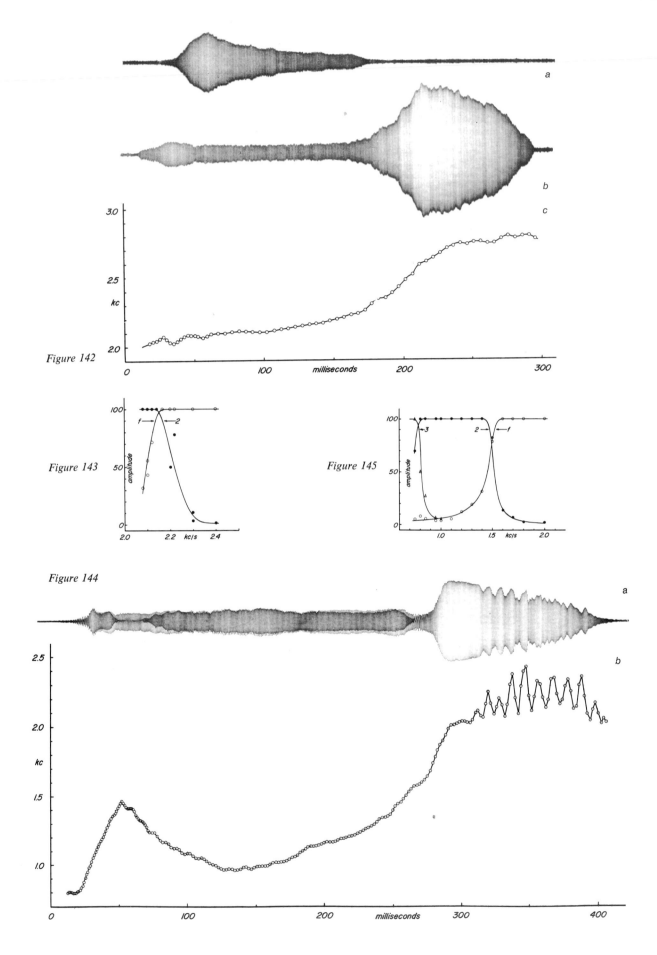

Figure 142

Figure 143

Figure 145

Figure 144

148

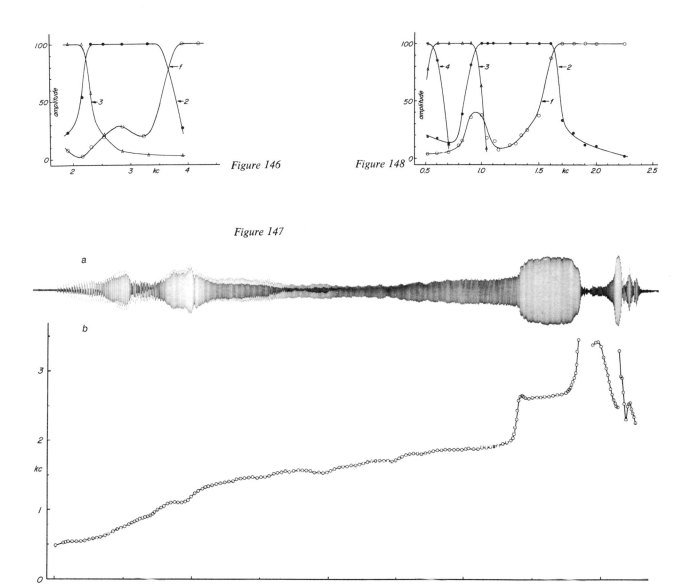

Figure 146

Figure 148

Figure 147

FIGURE 142. Song sparrow. Oscillograms: *a*, harmonic 2; *b*, fundamental. *c*, The frequencies are for the fundamental.

FIGURE 143. The song sparrow phrase from figure 142. Relative amplitude for the fundamental and harmonic 2 are plotted against fundamental frequency.

FIGURE 144. Brown thrasher: *a*, the unfiltered oscillogram; *b*, the frequency of the fundamental. The second harmonic disappears at 50 msec and again at 260 msec.

FIGURE 145. The brown thrasher phrase from figure 144. Relative amplitudes for harmonics 1, 2, and 3 are plotted against the frequency of the fundamental.

FIGURE 146. From a fragment of a phrase of the blue-gray gnatcatcher. Relative amplitudes for harmonics 1, 2, and 3 are plotted against the frequency of the fundamental.

FIGURE 147. Smooth-billed ani: *a*, the unfiltered oscillogram; *b*, the frequency of the fundamental.

FIGURE 148. The phrase of the smooth-billed ani from figure 147. Relative amplitudes for harmonics 1, 2, 3, and 4 are plotted against the frequency of the fundamental.

the several harmonics plotted against fundamental frequencies. The thresholds here are at 1.60 kc/s for fundamental and second harmonic, 0.95 kc/s for harmonics 2 and 3, 0.56 kc/s for harmonics 3 and 4. Again we see the characteristic sharpness of the several transitions.

I present the data from figures 143, 145, 146, and 148, together with a few additional examples, in table 14.

TABLE 14

	Transition frequencies for harmonics: kc/s		
	1–2	2–3	3–4
California quail		0.64	
a second phrase		0.71	
Leach's petrel	0.66		
European widgeon	1.75		
Yellow-shafted flicker		0.98	
Smooth-billed ani	1.63	0.95	0.56
Kiskadee flycatcher		0.85	
Blue jay	1.53	0.92	
Marsh tit	3.2		
Blue-gray gnatcatcher	3.7	2.2	
Icterine warbler			1.55
Brown thrasher	1.50	0.78	
Chalk-browed mockingbird	1.8		
Song sparrow	2.15		

In all cases relative amplitude/frequency plots show similar characteristics; a small frequency interval for each transition between harmonics, and a larger interval within which a particular harmonic will contain a relatively large fraction of the acoustic energy. For those glissandi embracing two or more transitions the frequency ratio for successive transitions is about 1.7, i.e., something less than an octave. Thus, for the smooth-billed ani the ratio 1.63:0.95 is 1.7, as is the ratio 0.95:0.56. The data are far too meager to establish the generality of the ratio.

We must now find a physiological explanation for these phenomena and one which does no violence to the anatomical model developed in previous chapters. The observed harmonic spectra might, for example, be generated at the source, the result of some steadily increasing nonlinearity in the vibration of the tympanic membrane as frequency (membrane tension) falls. They could also be due to some unspecified, source-generated harmonic spectrum, modulated by a tracheal resonance.

There appear to be sound criteria which eliminate the second hypothesis. Let us assume a source-generated harmonic spectrum of any form, whose fundamental frequency is steadily rising (or falling). A tracheal resonance might then modulate such a spectrum to eliminate all harmonics except those falling within the band-width of that resonance frequency. If this is indeed the correct acoustical mechanism, two criteria should be fulfilled: (a) a plot of relative amplitude against the *actual* frequency of the harmonic would peak at the tracheal resonance, and show a relatively narrow band-pass; (b) the mean frequency of the unfiltered signal should approximate the resonance frequency, irrespective of the frequency of the fundamental.

In Figures 149 and 150 are plots of relative amplitude against the frequency of the harmonic for the blue-gray gnatcatcher and the smooth-billed ani. We see immediately that the frequency range embracing 100% amplitude is wide, and that the "band-pass" at 50% relative amplitude is roughly 3.5 kc/s for the gnatcatcher, and 2.0 kc/s for the ani. In the latter case also, the points for the various harmonic amplitudes show much scatter, so much in fact that the mean line drawn on the figure has little significance. Such large values for the band-pass of the hypothetical tracheal resonance are at best unconvincing. Unfortunately tracheal lengths for the two birds are not available, but the band-pass values are so large that some of the calculated resonances might easily fall within the 100% amplitude peak.

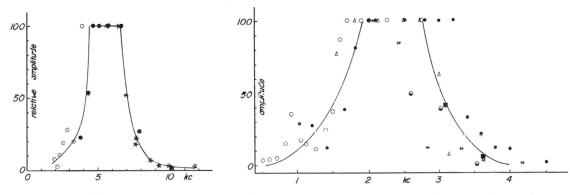

FIGURE 149. Blue-gray gnatcatcher. The relative amplitudes from figure 146 are plotted against the frequencies of the harmonics. Each symbol refers to a particular harmonic.

FIGURE 150. Smooth-billed ani. The relative amplitudes from figure 148 are plotted against the frequencies of the harmonics. Each symbol refers to a particular harmonic.

Figures 151 and 152 show unfiltered frequencies (filled circles) and fundamental frequencies (open circles) for the blue-gray gnatcatcher and the smooth-billed ani. If a resonance were involved, the unfiltered frequencies should be constant and approximate the resonance frequency, regardless of the value for the fundamental. We see immediately that the unfiltered frequencies are not constant, but parallel the fundamental frequency at the value for the corresponding dominant harmonic. For ready comparison the several harmonics of the fundamental are superimposed on the plot of unfiltered mean frequencies. Frequencies are plotted in logarithmic coordinates to show more clearly the equal slopes of the two curves.

In summary, we find no evidence for the presence of a tracheal resonance and must conclude that the harmonic spectra are source-generated and pass through the trachea without modulation. This is the situation as I have found it for whistled phrases; hence matched impedance of source and trachea must obtain also for frequencies below the harmonic threshold.

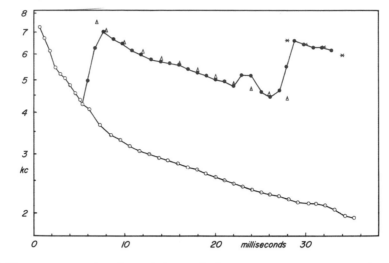

FIGURE 151. Blue-gray gnatcatcher. Open circles are the frequency of the fundamental. Filled circles are the frequency of the *unfiltered* signal. Triangles are twice, asterisks three times the fundamental frequency.

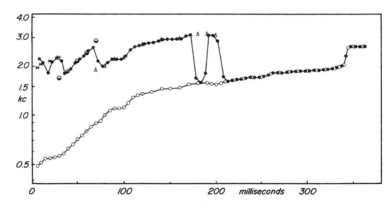

FIGURE 152. Smooth-billed ani. Open circles are the frequency of the fundamental. Filled circles are the frequency of the *unfiltered* signal. Asterisks are four times, half-filled circles three times, triangles twice the fundamental frequency.

To understand how source-generated harmonic spectra having these unusual characteristics can arise, we return to the diagrammatic sketch of the syrinx shown in figures 103 and 107. Imagine the tension in the tympanic membrane gradually reduced, the membrane at its vibrational peak approaching the opposing bronchial wall (or the external labium) more and more closely. The point will come when the bronchial wall will *constrain* the membrane thus forcing it to depart from a pure sinusoidal vibration. At this point the second harmonic will become evident, increasing in amplitude as membrane tension falls and the constraint of the opposing bronchial wall influences an increasing percentage of the period of vibration (the

period of the fundamental). As the process continues the amplitude of the fundamental will fall as that of the *second* harmonic rises. As membrane tension decreases
still further the second harmonic will become constrained and the *third* harmonic
will assume dominance. At this point the membrane can be visualized as undergoing
a *rippling* vibration, with a fundamental fixed by membrane tension, the associated
harmonic spectrum dictated by the *constraints* imposed by the passage within which
the membrane is vibrating.

One need not postulate actual contact of the membrane with the opposing bronchial wall, since constraints producing a departure from a sinusoidal vibratory mode
could arise even though air continues to flow through the syringeal passage.

Unfortunately I have not found glissandi for which the dominant harmonic is
higher than the fourth, hence can produce no transition diagrams showing the successive development of still higher harmonics. There are, however, a number of
calls for which the fundamental is constant and which have associated harmonic
spectra showing the characteristics described above, viz., a dominant harmonic with
adjacent harmonics falling off rapidly in relative amplitude.

See, for example, the harmonic spectrum for the red-breasted nuthatch (figure 5)
for which the fundamental is 500 c/s and the *fifth* harmonic is dominant. The spectrum for the scold call of the black-capped chickadee is shown in figure 87. Here
the fundamental is at 415 c/s and the *ninth* harmonic is dominant. For the scold
of the marsh tit, closely related to our chickadees, the fundamental is at 600 c/s and
the dominant harmonic is the *eighth*. Figure 153 is the spectrum for the red-throated
loon for which the fundamental frequency is 162 c/s and the *eighth* harmonic is

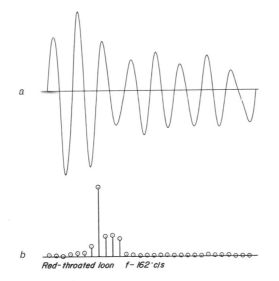

Red-throated loon   f- 162'c/s

FIGURE 153. Red-throated loon: *a*, the repetitive wave form;
b, the harmonic spectrum by Fourier transform.

dominant. (This harmonic spectrum was determined by computing the Fourier co-efficients for the repetitive wave form shown at the top of the figure.)

Table 15 shows a few additional harmonic spectra, principally for hawks and owls.

TABLE 15

	f, c/s	Harmonic						
		1	2	3	4	5	6	7
Red-shouldered hawk	1300	9	100	22	12	2		
Rough-legged hawk	1180	4	100	24	29	10	3	0.5
Killdeer	2200	10	100	12	2			
Screech owl	620	100	15	2				
Burrowing owl	800	100	38	8	2	1	1.5	
Long-eared owl	408	40	100	16	18	7		

In all of these cases we have harmonic spectra in which a single harmonic dominates, the amplitude falling off rapidly for lower and higher harmonics. We find for a particular species a threshold frequency below which harmonics appear, and a series of transition frequencies below the threshold, introducing the region within which successively higher harmonics become dominant. This process appears to carry on as frequency falls, at least to dominance of the ninth harmonic. For different species the frequency introducing the harmonic domain varies over wide limits and is presumably dependent on the thickness of the tympaniform membrane, viz., the thinner the membrane the higher the threshold. The harmonics are source-generated, arising out of the constraints imposed on the tympanic membrane vibrating in a confined space.

We consider now the controls available to the bird for varying the amplitude of its calls, and the character of the associated harmonic spectra.

First there is the *tension in the tympanic membrane*, applied through the syringeal muscles. As we have seen earlier, a change in membrane tension influences both frequency and amplitude, since relaxation of membrane tension, at a given pressure in the clavicular sac, will reduce frequency and at the same time will reduce the cross-section of the syringeal orifice, hence the amplitude of the signal.

Were this the sole controlling mechanism, we should find low amplitudes associated with all phrases having significant harmonic content, because the harmonic threshold always occurs at the lower end of the frequency range for a particular bird. There are, however, many calls, rich in harmonic content, with amplitudes quite as high as those for whistled phrases. Figure 154, for example, shows an oscillogram of the call of the black-capped chickadee. We see that the "scold" phrases, in which the ninth harmonic is dominant, have amplitudes nearly as high as those of the two introductory whistled phrases.

High amplitude, for phrases rich in harmonic content, must be associated with *increased pressure in the clavicular sac*. There is almost certainly an interrelationship between sac pressure, membrane tension, and the shape and position of the inwardly bowed vibrating membrane. At high membrane tensions, such as occur for whistled phrases, it is reasonable to suppose that the axis of the bowed membrane is perpendicular to the axis of the bronchial tube. Air flow, hence signal amplitude, will vary directly with the mean cross-section of the syringeal orifice, and with the square root of the pressure drop across the orifice. Increased sac pressure would increase the pressure drop across the syringeal orifice, but would at the same time reduce the cross-sectional area of the orifice by forcing the bowed membrane closer to the opposing bronchial wall (or external labium). The resultant of these opposing effects in influencing air flow, hence signal amplitude, is unpredictable, since there is no way in which we can measure membrane position as a function of sac pressure at a given membrane tension. The external labium, for those species possessing that organ, provides a much more effective method of controlling signal amplitude in whistled song, since by its insertion or withdrawal from the bronchial lumen, the area of the syringeal orifice, hence the air flow, can be increased or decreased without affecting the position of the vibrating membrane.

FIGURE 154. Black-capped chickadee. Unfiltered oscillogram of the scold call. The first two notes are whistled; in the last four the ninth harmonic is dominant.

At low membrane tensions, such as occur within the harmonic domain, one need no longer assume that the axis of the inwardly bowed membrane will remain perpendicular to the bronchial axis. For under these conditions the bowed membrane must surely become much less rigid and the resultant of the forces due to the sac pressure, and the pressure drop across the syringeal orifice, could force the bowed membrane to move in the direction of air flow somewhat as shown schematically in figure 155.

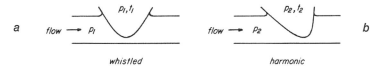

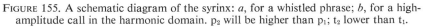

FIGURE 155. A schematic diagram of the syrinx: a, for a whistled phrase; b, for a high-amplitude call in the harmonic domain. p_2 will be higher than p_1; t_2 lower than t_1.

If this is indeed the case, the area of the syringeal orifice need not decrease as membrane tension is reduced and there would then be less, perhaps even no offset to the effect on signal amplitude of an increase in sac pressure.

No proof can be advanced to show unequivocally the effect of sac pressure in modifying signal amplitude, or the character of the associated harmonic spectrum. Nor can we say with certainty that the axis of the inwardly bowed membrane moves downstream with increasing sac pressure, permitting air flow to increase even though membrane tension is reduced. We can, however, show that harmonic-rich calls may have either high or low amplitudes, and for those rare cases where comparison can be made, a higher harmonic becomes dominant when the amplitude of the phrase increases. Table 16 shows two harmonic spectra for the kiskadee flycatcher, both with a fundamental frequency of 1380 c/s, the first from a fragment of the "song," the second from a "call." The amplitude of the call is four or five times that of the song fragment.

TABLE 16. Kiskadee Flycatcher

Relative Harmonic Amplitudes

	1	2	3	4	5	6	7	8
Song	13	100	14	9	6	3	1	
Call	10	59	77	100	36	2	5	1

The mechanism proposed for variation in signal amplitude within the harmonic domain is at least feasible, and not in conflict with the physiological and acoustical model developed to account for phenomena arising in whistled song. While the time constant involved in changing sac pressure is almost certainly too long to account for the very rapid modulations discussed in chapter 8, it is quite fast enough to permit changes from phrase to phrase, and even within a particular phrase.

We come finally to the *external labium* whose associated musculature permits its insertion into or withdrawal from the bronchial lumen. If the labium is inserted into the lumen, we would expect an increase in the threshold frequency below which harmonics occur, since the harmonic-producing mechanical constraints would arise at a higher frequency (higher membrane tensions). Movement of the labium into and out of the bronchial lumen could not, however, be used to control signal amplitude *within the harmonic region* since all that its insertion or withdrawal implies is a shift in the frequency at which mechanical constraints affect the sinusoidal character of membrane vibration.

To demonstrate the effect of a presumed change in position of the external labium figure 156 shows a phrase from the song of a mockingbird. In the figure, e shows the frequency of the fundamental. Of the four oscillograms (having the same time scale) a is unfiltered, b is the second harmonic, d is the fundamental. Figure 156c shows a short phrase produced by the second voice at about 3.8 kc/s, a small acoustical bonus, having nothing to do with the present argument.

Note that the fundamental for the entire phrase is constant at about 2.6 kc/s. In the low amplitude portion (10 to 140 msec) the fundamental and second harmonics have equal amplitudes. In the high amplitude portion (150 to 200 msec) the second harmonic disappears, and all of the acoustical energy is concentrated in the fundamental. We assume insertion of the labium into the lumen during the low amplitude portion of the phrase, inducing the appearance of harmonic 2 through constraint on the membrane. In the high amplitude portion the labium is withdrawn, removing the constraint, leaving the membrane free to vibrate at high amplitude without harmonic content. As indicated previously the second voice joins the performance, producing the short phrase at 3.8 kc/s, well away both from the fundamental at 2.6 kc/s and the harmonic at 5.2 kc/s.

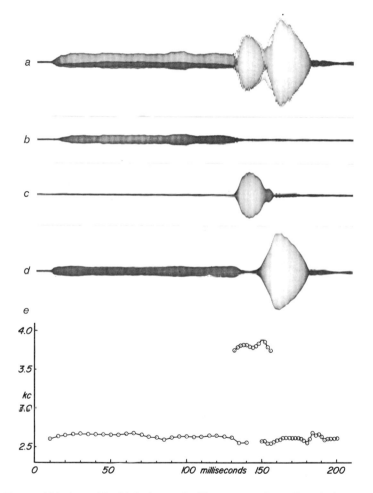

FIGURE 156. A mockingbird phrase. Oscillograms: *a*, the unfiltered phrase; *b*, the second harmonic; *c*, the second voice at 3.8 kc/s; *d*, the fundamental; *e*, the frequencies are for the fundamental.

Before summarizing the conclusions reached in this chapter we must consider two other manifestations in what we have called the "harmonic domain" in bird song.

It has been shown earlier that the relationships between fundamental frequency and the corresponding harmonic spectra cannot be attributed to tracheal modulation, but must arise as a result of mechanical constraints imposed on the vibrating tympanic membrane. We have in fact found *no* case in which the trachea influences either the harmonic spectrum or the loudness (amplitude) of the call. This is true even for those remarkable birds (cranes and swans for the most part) in which a substantial portion of the trachea is coiled within the body of the bird.

We take as an example the whooping crane. This bird has the longest trachea among the cranes, perhaps the longest among all birds. Coues (1903, p. 848, and in Berndt, 1911, p. 69) gives the length for two specimens as 127 and 147 cm. with roughly 50% of that length inside the body of the bird.

The record accompanying Peterson's "Field Guide for Western Birds" has whooping crane calls, three for the male and two for the female. In Table 17 I give the fundamental frequencies and corresponding harmonic spectra for each of these calls.

TABLE 17. Whooping Crane

Male	c/s		Relative Harmonic Amplitudes					
	F	f	1	2	3	4	5	6
1	953.9	954.2	64	35	100	27	6	1
2	937.8	946.8	100	49	58	19	3	
3	936.9	937.5	100	58	100	35	3.5	
Female								
1	1214.9	1214.9	100	20	9	2		
2	1216.6	1216.5	100	55	47	14		

F = The fundamental frequency isolated by filtration.
f = The unfiltered mean frequency.

In all cases frequency was determined by isolating the fundamental by filtration, then measuring the mean time intervals for 100 successive sinusoidal periods. Shown also is the mean *unfiltered* frequency measured in the same way. For the first male call, equally precise measurements were made for harmonics 2 and 3, for a small portion of the call, and the fundamental calculated by dividing the frequencies by 2 and 3, respectively. The fundamental frequencies so determined were 954.50, 954.41, 954.81 c/s from harmonics 1, 2, and 3, respectively.

I conclude that the harmonics are indeed precise integer multiples of the fundamental, and that the close correspondence of unfiltered frequency with the fundamental makes it at least unlikely that tracheal resonances are in any way involved.

As to the frequencies of the tracheal resonances, assuming trachea and source behave as a tube closed at one end and open at the other, the first resonance for the two specimens measured by Coues are at 70 and 60 c/s, respectively. Since no energy is found at frequencies below 930 c/s for the male, or 1130 c/s for the female, it is immediately apparent that the observed fundamental frequencies are source-generated. Taking the mean tracheal resonance at 65 c/s, the observed fundamental would fall at about the 14th tracheal resonance for the male, the 17th for the female. The higher harmonics for the male would occur at the 28th and 42nd resonance, and for the female at the 34th resonance.

In a damped resonator, resonance band-widths increase rapidly as one moves to higher resonances. Table 18 shows the band-widths given by Fant (1960, p. 126) for the resonances of human oral cavities set to pronounce the vowel [α].

TABLE 18. Resonance Frequencies and Band-widths for the Vowel [α]

Resonance	Frequency c/s	Band Width c/s
1	630	57
2	1070	72
3	2400	130
4	3550	175
5	4000	200

We have no quantitative data on the damping of the crane's trachea, but it cannot be substantially less than that of the human oral cavities (wall stiffness and frictional factors should be of the same order of magnitude). It should be safe to conclude that the band-width of resonances ranging from the 14th to the 42nd would be so wide that the source-generated signal would pass through without change.

For a more familiar but not necessarily more revealing analogy we can compare the cranes' trachea, 50 to 60 inches in length, to the length of an orchestral trumpet, one example of which has a length of 58½ in. The trumpet has a range of approximately 175 to 700 c/s. The upper limit is well below the fundamental for the male and female cranes. It would take a highly skilled performer to make his trumpet "speak" at "whooper" frequencies.

We conclude that the whooping crane calls are source-generated, and are neither modulated or reinforced by the trachea.

We turn now to two swans, the whistling swan and the trumpeter swan. The birds appear to be dimensionally similar, the latter somewhat longer (65 in) than the former (52½ in). Kortright's (1942, p. 69) figure shows that both have a portion of the trachea coiled within the body. Unfortunately no data on tracheal length appear in the literature. Table 19 gives fundamental frequencies and harmonic spectra for two calls of the whistling swan (sex unknown), and figure 157 shows the repetitive wave form, the corresponding harmonic spectrum (by Fourier transform) and the frequency of the fundamental for the trumpeter.

The unfiltered mean frequencies for the two calls correspond precisely with the frequency of the dominant second harmonic (see table 20).

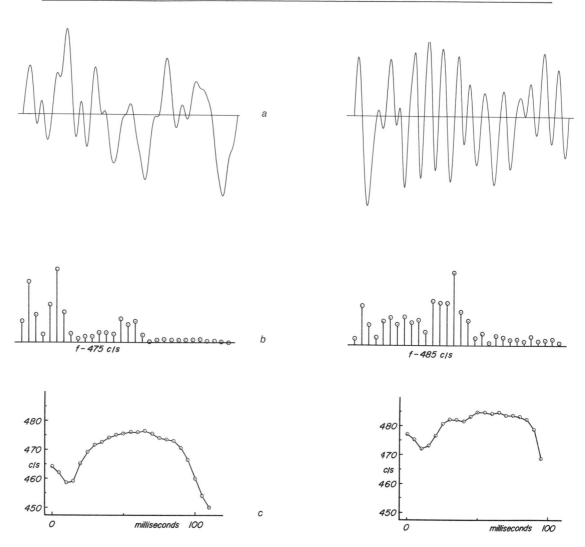

FIGURE 157. Two calls of the trumpeter swan: *a*, the repetitive wave forms; *b*, the corresponding harmonic spectra by Fourier transform; *c*, the frequency of the fundamental for the whole call, isolated by filtration.

TABLE 19. Whistling Swan									TABLE 20		
Call	Frequency	Relative Harmonic Amplitudes							Call	Harmonic 2	Unfiltered
	c/s	1	2	3	4	5	6			c/s	c/s
1	815	39	100	54	7	5	3		1	1630.9	1630.5
2	833	28	100	38	5	3	2		2	1665.9	1665.3

For the whistling swan the argument against tracheal modulation is as compelling as for the whooping crane; in fact the observed harmonic spectrum resembles even more closely the spectra produced by "membrane constraint," found among the

Passeriformes. We might guess the tracheal length as not less than 60 cm, corresponding to a first tracheal resonance of about 150 c/s. The dominant second harmonic would then correspond to the 11th resonance frequency. Alternatively, if the observed fundamental were to correspond with the first tracheal resonance, the trachea could be no longer than 11 cm, a manifest absurdity.

In figure 156 for the trumpeter swan, we find a much less tidy situation; the corresponding harmonic spectra is far more extensive and complex than any we have examined previously. We see also that the wave forms and spectra for the two calls are quite different, even though fundamental frequencies differ by only 10 c/s.

One could perhaps argue that the high amplitudes for harmonics 2 and 6 in the first call provide evidence for tracheal resonance. A first resonance at 950 c/s would, however, require a tracheal length of about 9 cm, an impossible value. Furthermore the second call shows completely different harmonic amplitudes, the maximum appearing at the 15th harmonic with apparently random amplitude variations above and below it.

When we compare the calls for the two swans the case for tracheal modulation becomes even less tenable. The trumpeter is about 25 percent longer than the whistler, and the two trachea are in roughly equal proportion. If tracheal resonances were dominant, one would expect the trumpeter to sound at a somewhat lower frequency than the whistler, but with generally similar harmonic spectra. This is clearly not the case.

We must then conclude, as for the whooping crane, that the calls for both swans are source-generated, and are unaffected in their passage through the trachea. The argument has been advanced (Berndt, 1938, p. 113) that since all birds with a portion of their trachea coiled within the body, have loud voices, the long trachea must be in some way responsible. This is not a particularly convincing hypothesis. Swans and cranes are large birds, and their sac system must have a correspondingly large volume. A loud sound must in the last analysis be due to a pulsating air flow at high mass velocity and this could easily be supplied from a sac system of high capacity without tracheal assistance.

For the whistling swan the spectra closely resemble those found for the Passeriformes, and it seems safe to conclude that they arise out of a mild constraint imposed on the vibrating membrane by the opposing bronchial walls. The whistling swan was not sufficiently obliging to sing a glissando; hence we cannot show that harmonic spectra develop according to the pattern found for other species. The similarity, however, is at least suggestive, and at best conclusive that the same mechanism is involved in both cases.

For the trumpeter swan we must assume a much more potent constraint on the membrane, producing an approach to the pulses generated in the human glottis. This is not a departure in kind but only in degree from the relatively mild constraints encountered previously. We assume a somewhat thicker membrane, perhaps an increased sac pressure, and a transition from the rippling type of membrane movement to one more closely resembling a pulsing vibration, the fundamental still dependent on membrane tension. The more nearly one approaches a simple pulse the more terms one will find in the harmonic spectrum. The extreme case (a sharp pulse of very short duration) will produce a harmonic spectrum containing an infinite number of terms at constant amplitudes. The trumpeter must produce a pulsing vibration somewhere within this range, viz., a sharp initial pulse followed by rippling vibrations of smaller amplitude. One would expect such a pulsing vibration to be quite sensitive to small changes in sac pressure and membrane tension. This may account for the large differences in harmonic spectra for the two calls of the trumpeter swan.

There must also be a radiation effect as the sound leaves the trachea at the laryngeal opening. When the wave length is large as compared with the tracheal diameter, radiation effects will be such as to produce an increase in amplitude with increasing frequency. The amplitude boost could reach values approaching 6 db per octave. We know virtually nothing about radiation at larynx and mouth cavity hence have no basis for reconstructing the pulse shape at the syrinx from the recorded wave form. For our present argument this incapability makes little difference. We wish merely to show that there is no tracheal modulation, thus leaving the neck of the bird free to pursue its other essential functions without influencing vocalization.

The pulsing type of source vibration, characteristic of the trumpeter swan, is most frequently encountered among the Anatidae. Many examples could be presented; three are offered here.

Figure 158 is the repetitive wave form of the mallard. Here the fundamental frequency is 179 c/s and the wave form reasonably regular. The 12th harmonic is dominant and the harmonic spectrum is not too different from that of the black-capped chickadee or marsh tit.

At the other extreme figure 159 illustrates two calls of the Canada goose. These are in fact two subphrases of the same call, the first with a fundamental at 382 c/s, the second (the longer part) with a fundamental at 131 c/s. Note the extreme irregularity of both wave forms, apparently comprising an initial short pulse of high amplitude followed by a low amplitude ripple of irregular repetition rate. Note also the general similarity of the first third of the 131 c/s wave form to the entire wave form at 382 c/s.

As a final example figure 160 shows the calls of the male (*a*) and female (*b*) of the common teal. The call of the male is a pure whistled phrase without harmonic content. The female, on the other hand, has a call somewhat reminiscent of that of the mallard but at a higher fundamental frequency, with the 12th harmonic dominant.

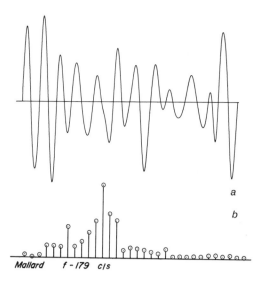

Mallard   f - 179 c/s

FIGURE 158. Mallard: *a*, the repetitive wave form;
b, the harmonic spectrum by Fourier transform.

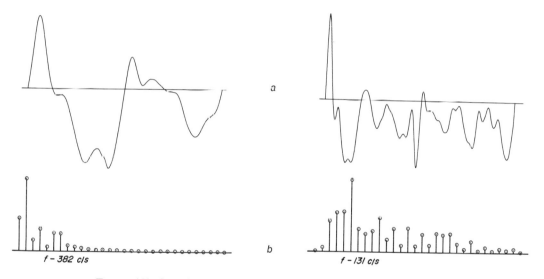

f - 382 c/s

f - 131 c/s

FIGURE 159. Canada goose. Two subphrases of a single call: *a*, repetitive
wave forms; *b*, harmonic spectra by Fourier transform.

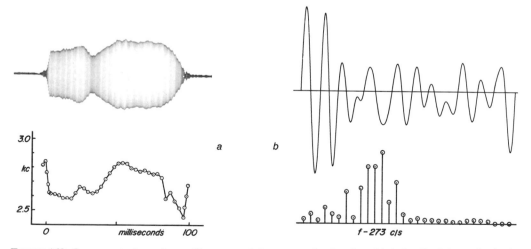

f - 273 c/s

FIGURE 160. Common teal: *a*, the oscillogram and frequency plot for the whistled call of the male; *b*, the
repetitive wave form and the harmonic spectrum by Fourier transform, for the female.

We proceed now with our summary.

For many birds—perhaps for all birds—there is a threshold frequency below which harmonics arise, above which the phrases are whistled without harmonic content. The threshold frequency varies widely among species, from a value below 500 c/s for the barred owl, to about 4000 c/s for the blue-gray gnatcatcher. We assume this variation to be related to the thickness of the tympanic membrane, the thinner the membrane the higher the frequency at the harmonic threshold.

As the frequency falls below the threshold value the second harmonic appears, increasing in relative amplitude as the amplitude of the fundamental falls. The frequency range traversed while dominance transfers from first to second harmonic is very small, a few hundred cycles per second. There follows a frequency interval (amounting to something less than an octave) in which the second harmonic remains dominant, after which there is a second transition, during which the third harmonic becomes dominant as the second harmonic falls in amplitude. The process continues with falling frequency, with successively higher harmonics attaining dominance up to at least the ninth harmonic.

The resulting harmonic spectra *always* show dominance of a particular harmonic with amplitude falling off rapidly for adjacent harmonics.

The harmonic spectra cannot be due to tracheal modulation of a source-generated signal, but arise within the syrinx as a result of mechanical constraints imposed on the vibrating tympanic membrane by the opposing bronchial wall. The resulting departure from simple harmonic motion in the vibrating membrane gives rise to successively higher harmonics as membrane tension (fundamental frequency) falls. The membrane vibration approaches a "rippling" form, the fundamental controlled by membrane tension, the rapidity of the "ripple" dictating the particular harmonic whose amplitude will be dominant. The membrane need not actually strike the opposing bronchial wall to produce these effects; one merely need postulate a constraint giving rise to progressively increasing nonlinearity in membrane vibration.

The value of the threshold frequency can be varied by insertion or withdrawal of the external labium (where one exists) within the bronchial lumen. Insertion of the labium will increase the threshold frequency.

The amplitude of the call can be modified by changing pressure in the clavicular sac; the amplitudes of calls in the harmonic domain can be quite as high as those of whistled phrases. There is evidence to indicate that increased amplitudes in the harmonic domain are associated with spectra in which a higher harmonic is dominant.

Among the Anatidae, harmonic spectra are found which contain many terms, with amplitudes showing no particular pattern. Such spectra must be associated with a form of membrane vibration approaching the pulses produced in the human glottis. The observed spectra are compatible with a repetitive wave form comprising a high amplitude pulse followed by a series of less violent ripples of variable period.

Throughout the harmonic domain, whatever the species and whatever form the wave form or harmonic spectrum may take, the evidence shows quite clearly that there is no tracheal modulation; the call is produced in the syrinx and passes unchanged through the trachea.

Finally the harmonic domain is a logical, perhaps an inevitable extension of the acoustical and physiological model developed in previous chapters. Any bird, if it chooses, can produce either whistled phrases, or phrases of variable harmonic content. Some elect to sing only whistled phrases, some confine their vocalization to the harmonic domain, many move back and forth from one to the other. The two voices produced in the two acoustical sources may both operate in the whistled or in the harmonic domain. We find cases where one voice is whistled, the other produces a harmonic spectrum. One finds also rapid modulations, such as have been described in chapter 8, within the harmonic domain; but here frequency/amplitude coupling, combined with a frequency dependent harmonic spectrum, produces spectrograms and oscillograms so complex as to defy detailed analysis.

Chapter 11   TALKING BIRDS

We come, finally, to those birds which produce a more or less convincing imitation of the human voice. Our task is to determine whether such birds invoke, when "talking," some completely new physiological and acoustical mechanism or whether they achieve their imitations with the same apparatus and the same acoustical processes which are involved when they sing their normal songs.

The ability (perhaps we should say the willingness) to imitate the human voice is limited to a very few species. Jeffery Boswall has been kind enough to send me a tape prepared by the British Broadcasting Company which presents a number of examples of talking birds. These include a canary, a house sparrow, several parrots, and the Indian hill myna. The performances were quite spotty. One could readily hear that the canary and house sparrow were trying to talk, but it was difficult to distinguish words, and one could scarcely call their performance an imitation of the human voice. For the parrots, words and phrases were clearly understandable, but one would not be deceived into thinking that a human was actually speaking. The mynas, on the other hand, were really extraordinary. Their phrases were clear and well defined, and making due allowance for "accent," one could easily imagine that the phrases were being spoken by a male voice.

The literature on talking birds is scanty; in fact I have been able to find only one paper (Thorpe, 1959) which discusses the acoustics and physiology involved when birds imitate humans. Thorpe concludes that because a myna produces vowel sounds which when analyzed by the sound spectrograph show patterns generally similar to those for human vowels, the acoustical processes involved must necessarily be the same.

166

It would seem to me that this conclusion is open to serious question since it implies that any really good imitation must a priori involve use of an identical acoustical mechanism.

I remember years ago a British actor (if I have successfully dredged my memory his name was Reginald Gardiner), whose tour de force was imitations of humans, of animals, and frequently of inanimate objects. It has been a long time since I have seen him perform but I remember clearly a completely convincing imitation of a steam locomotive arriving and leaving a railroad station. Manifestly Mr. Gardiner did not have a steam engine in his interior; hence one must assume that he used his own vocal apparatus in a manner that was convincing enough to impress the attentive (and enthralled) audience.

By the same token one cannot say that the myna employs, in "talking," a replica of the human vocal apparatus for it is equally possible that the bird can control its tympaniform membranes to produce an imitation of human speech without the resonating cavities employed by humans.

It may be as well to review once more, and in some detail, the physiological and acoustical processes involved in human speech, since these must of necessity provide the criteria against which to appraise the myna imitation.

Voiced speech sounds begin at the glottis, located at the anterior end of the trachea, behind that feature of human anatomy somewhat inelegantly called the "Adam's apple." The glottis comprises a pair of muscles disposed across the end of the trachea to form a slit-like opening. When these muscles are relaxed the end of the trachea remains open and we exhale and inhale normally. When the muscles are in tension the glottal slit closes momentarily while pressure is built up in the lungs. When the pressure is increased to a sufficiently high value (equivalent to 4–8 in of water), the glottal slit is forced open and a puff of air is released. The slit then closes, aided perhaps by the Bernoulli effect of the flowing air, and stays closed until the pressure builds again to the required value. We have then a series of puffs of air whose frequency is controlled by muscle tension, each puff comprising perhaps 40 percent of the period between puffs; the glottal slit is closed for the remaining 60 percent of the period. These repetitive puffs of air are modulated in passing through oral and nasal cavities and the result is speech or song. The fundamental frequency of the resulting sound is controlled solely by the tension in the glottal muscles; linguistics and tonal quality are dictated by particular arrangements of the oral and nasal cavities, and by the position of lips, tongue, and teeth.

Acoustically the speech process may be described in terms of frequency and amplitude, or on a scale involving merely time and amplitude. The two processes are equivalent, and one is readily converted to the other by Fourier transformations.

Let us assume that a man is enunciating the vowel "a." He will set his glottal muscles to a given tension and so will produce a series of puffs of air at a frequency which for the male voice will lie between 80 and 180 puffs per second. In time-amplitude coordinates there will be a rapid rise and fall in amplitude (air flow) occurring in the first 40 percent of the period, then zero amplitude until the next puff occurs, the process repeating itself for whatever time period the vowel is being spoken. A Fourier transform of this repetitive wave form produces a harmonic spectrum, for which the fundamental corresponds to the period between puffs; for which the amplitude is maximum for the fundamental frequency; and in which the amplitude of successive harmonics decays at a rate corresponding roughly to 12 db per octave.

This acoustical disturbance, created in the glottis, then passes through the oral cavities, through the speaker's lips, and so to the ears of the listener. In that passage the glottal puffs are modulated by virtue of the resonances characteristic of the oral cavities which the speaker has so fashioned that the end result will be the vowel "a." In time-amplitude coordinates the glottal puffs will stimulate damped sinusoidal wave forms at each of the resonances characteristic of the oral cavity. Each wave form will have a frequency equal to the resonance frequency; the amplitude will decay exponentially for a time corresponding to the period of the fundamental; the rate of decay will depend on the damping, i.e., the band-pass, of the resonator. The wave form for the resulting vowel sound will be the sum of the stimulated wave forms at all resonances of the oral cavities.

The process can be stated somewhat more simply in terms of frequencies and amplitudes. The harmonic spectrum equivalent to the repetitive glottal pulses (the spectrum at the source) will be modulated in passing through the oral cavities in a way which reinforces those source frequencies falling within the range of each cavity resonance, and attenuates all other source frequencies.

Our oral cavities can be controlled by appropriate positioning of tongue and lips to produce a wide variety of vowel sounds, each associated with its own series of resonances. In acoustical terminology the resonances produced in the oral cavities are called formants. The fact should be emphasized that the oral cavities are complex in form; hence their resonances will not have the integer relationships characteristic of the resonances of a simple tube; the ratio of successive resonances will vary over wide limits, depending upon the vowel which is being enunciated.[23]

We see at once a serious difficulty in equating myna acoustics to our own. For the only resonator available to the myna is its trachea, a simple tube whose resonances would have integer relationships with each other. (The mouth cavity of the bird is small and its resonances would be at frequencies substantially above those encountered in human speech.) While the trachea is extensible over narrow limits, its resonances would remain in fixed relationship to each other, e.g., at 1, 3, 5, etc., times the

23. This discussion is admittedly abbreviated, but serves adequately as a basis for appraising differences between myna and human speech sounds. For more detailed treatment of human speech, see Fant (1960), Pierce and David (1958), and Joos (1948).

first resonance for a tube closed at one end and open at the other, or at 1, 2, 3, etc., times the first resonance for a tube open at both ends. There appear to be no physiological resources available to the bird which would produce the infinitely variable and complex resonating cavities available to humans.

We proceed now to a detailed analysis of myna and human "speech." We have selected the myna for comparison because it gives the most convincing imitation of human speech of all talking birds. Unfortunately, the myna on the BBC tape speaks with a British accent which neither my wife nor I can duplicate. We have, however, selected for analysis a phrase—"pretty well, Charlie"—in which accent appears suppressed to an extent which should not greatly influence human comparisons with the myna's rendition. Figures 161–163, show for Mrs. Greenewalt and me, and for the myna, sonagrams of the phrase, together with bar contour spectrograms prepared by Mr. D. J. MacLean of the Bell Telephone Laboratories.

Manifestly there are differences between the myna and the human spectrograms, but one cannot say with certainty that they imply a different acoustical mechanism for the myna. For example, one sees that in the myna spectrogram the energy content of the fundamental and the first two or three harmonics is relatively small as compared to the two humans. Furthermore while the quality of the myna's voice is clearly that of a human male, its fundamental is in the female range, in some cases as much as an octave above the fundamental in my rendition. These differences, while real enough, are difficult to interpret in acoustical terms; hence it is necessary to turn to the underlying wave forms for additional and hopefully more conclusive evidence.

For this evaluation the vowel "a" in "Charlie" was selected. The repetitive wave form was displayed on the face of the oscilloscope, a photograph made, and time-amplitude coordinates (about 100 points) taken from the photograph. The coordinates were presented to a computer which was asked to derive a Fourier series which would embrace the first thirty harmonics. After the computer had performed its task, the results were fed to an instrument called a "Calcomp"[24] which redrew the original wave form in accordance with instructions from the computer. The result is considerably more elegant than the original photograph and much easier to obtain than a laborious replotting of the time-amplitude coordinates.

Figure 164 shows the wave forms and corresponding harmonic spectra for the myna, and for Mrs. Greenewalt and me. As to the wave forms, it is difficult in photographing the face of the oscilloscope to place the axis of symmetry in its proper position. The computer finds this axis in the course of its calculations, and it is properly placed in the figure. This is why the depicted wave forms do not start at zero amplitude.

We see immediately that the wave form for the myna is quite different from those

24. Manufactured by California Computer Products, Inc., Anaheim, California.

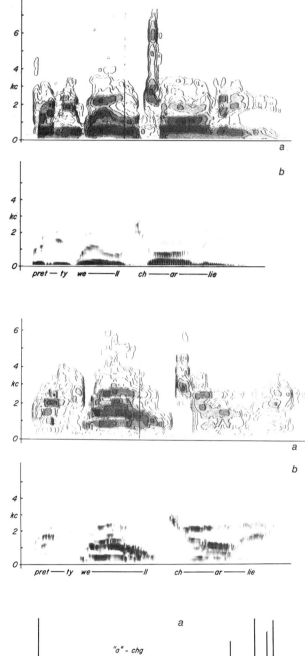

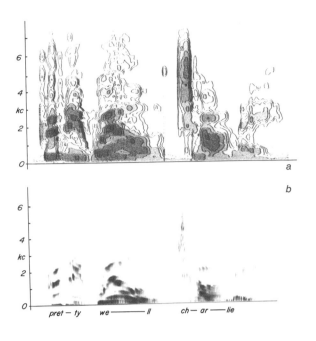

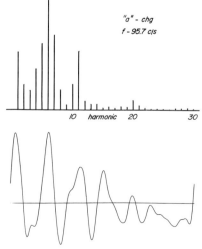

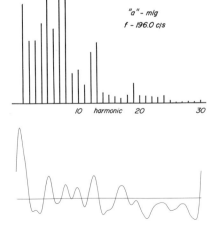

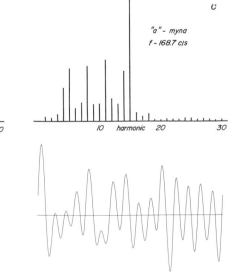

above left

FIGURE 161. The phrase "Pretty well, Charlie" spoken by the author (CHG): *a*, contour spectrogram; *b*, sonagram.

above right

FIGURE 162. The phrase "Pretty well, Charlie" spoken by Mrs. Greenewalt (MLG): *a*, contour spectrogram; *b*, sonagram.

left

FIGURE 163. The phrase "Pretty well, Charlie" spoken by the myna: *a*, contour spectrogram; *b*, sonagram.

below

FIGURE 164. Wave forms and the corresponding harmonic spectra for a single fundamental period taken from the vowel "a" in "Charlie": *a*, CHG; *b*, MLG; *c*, myna.

for the humans. Both human wave forms show a substantial decay in amplitude within the fundamental period and much less regularity in the sinusoids within the wave form. These differences are, of course, carried over to the derived harmonic spectra which also show formant locations quite clearly. For the humans, harmonic amplitudes tend to fall with rising harmonic number; for the myna maximum amplitude is found at the fifteenth harmonic. In table 21 we show formants and the corresponding harmonic amplitudes for the three voices.

TABLE 21. The "a" in "Charlie"

Formant	C.H.G.		Myna		M.L.G.	
	Frequency (c/s)	Amplitude	Frequency (c/s)	Amplitude	Frequency (c/s)	Amplitude
1	575	100	840	43.2	980	100
2	1050	48.0	1350	45.1	1560	98.8
3	1900	7.7	1860	50.7	2550	50.2
4			2530	100	3720	16.7
Frequency of fundamental c/s	95.7		168.7		196.0	

We have made the same analysis for the vowel "e" in "well." The results are shown in table 22, the harmonic spectra, without the associated wave forms in figure 165.

TABLE 22. The "e" in "well"

Formant	C.H.G.		Myna		M.L.G.	
	Frequency (c/s)	Amplitude	Frequency (c/s)	Amplitude	Frequency (c/s)	Amplitude
1	490	100	840	100	513	100
2	1390	12.5	1400	80.5	1540	32.6
3	2130	9.0	2520	47.1	2560	25.3
Frequency of fundamental (c/s)	168.7		280.6		256.4	

In the vowel "e" the same anomalies are present for the myna as for the vowel "a." The wave form is different in character and the energy in the fundamental and second harmonic is relatively low. While the energy in this case drops off with increasing formant number, the decay is less rapid than for the human examples. It will be seen also that the formant frequencies for the human examples are roughly in the ratio 1:3:5, whereas the myna formants (as for the vowel "a") bear no integer relationship with each other.

The comparison so far of myna with human speech has revealed differences which appear substantial and significant, but we have as yet no proof that the myna uses a different acoustical process. For that proof it is necessary to examine formant wave forms.

Two methods are available for deriving wave forms associated with particular formants. One must first select from the harmonic spectrum the frequency range embracing the formant in question, viz., for the vowel "a" in my rendition one selects terms 3 to 8 for formant 1; 9 to 14 for formant 2; and 17 to 23 for formant 3. The first method involves setting filters to embrace these terms successively and photographing the resulting wave form (for a given period) on the face of the oscilloscope. In the second method one simply instructs the computer and Calcomp, respectively, to determine coordinates for the sum of the appropriate terms (taking into account both phase and amplitude) from the original harmonic spectrum, and to plot the result. I have used the latter method first because it is the least arduous, and secondly, the filters, because of the time delay inherent in their use, can alter the original phase relationships to produce a distorted result.

Figure 166 shows wave forms associated with the first three formants in my rendition of the vowel "a," and figure 167 the four myna formants for the same vowel. We see that the wave forms for the human formants all show a decay in amplitude within the fundamental period, whereas the myna formants do not. For easy visibility the Calcomp was asked to draw all wave forms at the same maximum amplitude; the actual relative amplitudes for the dominant harmonics in each formant region are given in table 21.

Figure 168 shows the time-amplitude coordinates for successive half-sinusoids in the wave form corresponding to my first formant as well as the reciprocal period ("instantaneous frequency") for successive half-sinusoids. A line representing an exponential decay has been fitted to the amplitude data; the fit is good for the greater part of the fundamental period. The corresponding band-pass for this first resonance is 63 c/s; its frequency corresponds closely to that of the sixth harmonic. For the other formants the decay is exponential for only a portion of the fundamental period; for the portion that can be fitted to an exponential decay, the band-pass for the second formant is about 100 c/s, and for the third between 200 and 300 c/s, both reasonable values. The irregularity of the decay for the second and third formants may be due either to radiation effects as the sound passes the lips, to phase changes associated with those radiation effects, or more probably to the fact that definition of a wave form having an exponential decay requires more terms in the Fourier series than are found between successive resonances, thus leading to an overlap in the terms defining successive formants. Because of the low amplitudes of formants 2 and 3, such effects would be relatively greater than with the dominant first formant. The important point, however, is that in all cases the amplitude for the human formants decays within the fundamental period; for the myna it does not.

Here then is the first real evidence that resonators are *not* involved in the myna imitation. Stimulation of a resonance as a result of an acoustical disturbance must produce a wave form in which the amplitude decays within the fundamental period; were there no decay in amplitude one would have to assume no damping of the resonator and an infinitely small band-pass for the resonator considered as a filter.

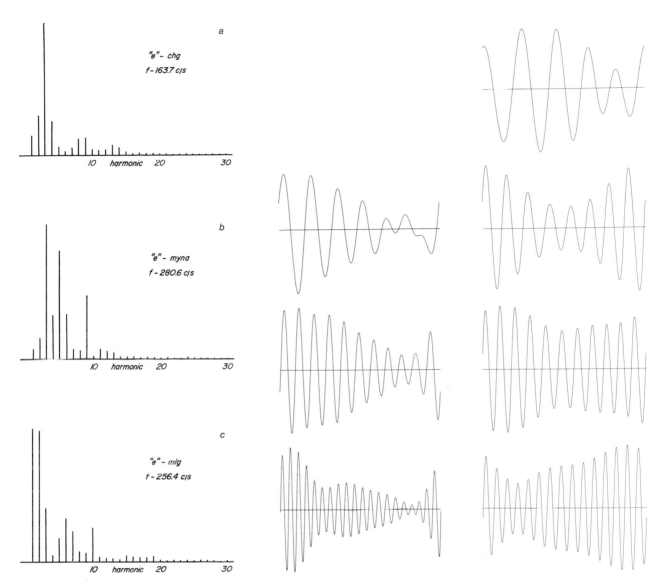

FIGURE 165. Harmonic spectra for a single fundamental period taken from the vowel "e" in "well": *a*, CHG; *b*, myna; *c*, MLG.

FIGURE 166. Wave forms for the first three formants from CHG's rendition of the vowel "a" in "Charlie."

FIGURE 167. Wave forms for the first four formants from the myna's rendition of the vowel "a" in "Charlie."

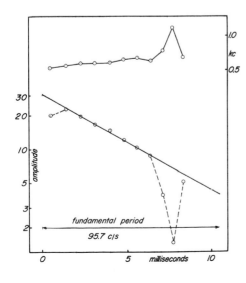

FIGURE 168. The first formant in CHG's rendition of "a" in "Charlie." The amplitude of successive half-sinusoids (negative values plotted as if they were positive). The solid line is an exponential decay fitted to the data; its slope corresponds to a band-pass for the resonator of 63 c/s. "Instantaneous" frequencies derived from the period for successive half-sinusoids. The mean frequency for those points fitting the exponential decay is 600 c/s, just above the sixth harmonic.

One would not expect the myna's trachea to be less damped than the human oral cavities; both comprise soft and relatively yielding walls. Furthermore an undamped resonator would imply feedback and control of the source, which would then be forced to vibrate at the frequencies of the resonator. There would be no possibility of a substantial change in formant frequencies from vowel to vowel, hence "speech" sounds could not be produced.

Given the length of the myna trachea, it is possible to compare the "formant" frequencies of myna speech with those resonances which are theoretically possible. Peter Ames has determined the tracheal length of the myna to be 64 mm, equivalent to a first resonance at 1400 c/s if the trachea during vocalization is closed at one end and open at the other, or a first resonance of 2800 c/s if the trachea behaves as a tube open at both ends. Table 23 compares the myna formants in the vowels "a" and "e" with the calculated resonances.

TABLE 23

Formant	Formant Frequencies for the Vowel		Resonance Frequencies for a 64-mm Tube	
	"a"	"e"	Closed one end	Open both ends
1	850	840	1400	2800
2	1350	1400	4200	5600
3	1860	2520	6900	8400
4	2530			

It is apparent that the formant frequencies do not match the resonance frequencies. All observed formants fall below the second resonance for a 64-mm tube closed at one end, open at the other, and below the first resonance for a tube open at both ends. Even if we disregard the tracheal length, the observed formants have neither a 1:3:5 or a 2:4:6 relationship. One must conclude, then, from this and the evidence of the wave forms that resonances are not involved in myna "speech."

The wave form is the primary acoustical manifestation; the Fourier transform is its exact counterpart only if phase as well as amplitude of the component harmonics is taken into account. Neither the sound spectrogram nor the human ear are sensitive to changes in phase, hence the spectrogram of the vowel "a" for the myna in figure 161 could be produced from an infinite number of underlying wave forms, and the sound to the human ear would be the same. A source disturbance modulated by resonances is not essential in producing what to our ears is an adequate rendition of the vowel "a" (or any other vowel); the same effect could be produced by any appropriate wave form so long as the equivalent harmonic spectrum (neglecting phase) roughly approximates that of the human voice. The approximations can be quite rough; it has been shown at the Bell Telephone Laboratories that much of the voice spectrum is redundant even if the criterion is recognition of the speech of a particular individual. If the criterion is merely comprehension of words and phrases, then more details of the voice spectrum can be disregarded. The task of the myna in imitating speech sounds is not as difficult as might be supposed; he need only produce at his tympanic membranes a wave form giving a reasonable approximation of the human spectrum.

It remains now to answer the final question: if myna speech does not involve resonances modulating a source spectrum, how is the imitation produced? Here we can only speculate, for while at least reasonably conclusive evidence has been produced to show absence of resonances, no method has been devised by which one can demonstrate what actually happens. It has been seen in the previous chapter, however, that birds can produce a limited harmonic spectrum by reducing membrane tension to provide a given fundamental and by positioning the external labium to control the location of the dominant harmonic. One can then imagine both tympaniform membranes set to give the same fundamental frequency, and by appropriate positioning of the two external labia to produce two spectra simultaneously, each with a different dominant harmonic. This acoustical maneuver would show on the sound spectrogram as two distinct formants. If more were required, the *phase* of the fundamental frequency of one of the membranes could be shifted with respect to the other to produce a periodic attenuation in harmonic amplitude. If, for example, the phase of the two fundamentals were shifted by one quarter of a period, every fourth harmonic would be attenuated. It looks very much as if something of the sort were happening in the myna rendition of the vowel "a." We see amplitude minima at harmonics 2, 6, 9.5, 13, and 17, the interval averaging just under four harmonics. Such minima would be produced if the fundamental were shifted by one quarter of a period between the two membranes. The period corresponding to a frequency of 168.7 c/s is approximately 6 msec. As previously noted, the time perception of the bird should be able to cope with a period shift of 1.5 msec.

All of this sounds quite complicated, but scarcely more so than the acoustical maneuvering involved in human speech. I would postulate only three points of control: the tension in the tympaniform membranes for a given fundamental; the positioning of the external labia for the dominant harmonics; and the phase difference, i.e., the time lag between fundamental periods to produce additional "formants."

I conclude then that birds can "talk" using nothing more than the anatomical features and acoustical techniques employed in normal song. Even here I can find no evidence for the presence of modulating resonances; it would appear that all bird sounds, normal or imitative, are generated solely within the syrinx.

Chapter 12 SUMMARY

We come, at last, to a summary of this rather long account. We begin it by noting that the physiology and acoustics of bird vocalization are unique in the animal kingdom for at least three reasons:

Sound is produced at the syrinx in an air stream modulated by an elastic membrane vibrating in a restricted passage bounded by the walls of the bronchus. This source-generated acoustical disturbance appears not to be modified in its passage through the trachea.

The syrinx contains two independently controllable sources, one in each bronchus, enabling the bird to produce two notes or phrases simultaneously.

These sounds can be modulated, in either frequency, or in amplitude, or more usually in both, with extraordinary rapidity, so rapidly in fact that human ears cannot perceive the modulations as such, receiving instead an impression of notes of varying quality or timbre.

I discuss first the Oscine syrinx, because it is the most elaborate in an acoustical sense, and because the Oscines embrace nearly half the total number of avian species. With the Oscines as a point of departure we may consider the acoustical significance of the simplifications in syringeal structure encountered in other groups of birds.

The syrinx, as we have seen, is surrounded by the interclavicular sac. Increasing the air pressure in this sac forces the internal tympaniform membrane into the bronchial lumen. Tension applied to the membrane by the syringeal muscles, in opposition to the sac pressure, produces a constricted passage in the bronchus. Air from the lungs flowing past this constriction causes the membrane to vibrate. If the membrane is so positioned that it can vibrate without constraint, the vibration will be sinusoidal, without higher harmonics, and at a frequency which will depend on membrane tension and on the mass per unit cross-section of the membrane itself. There are three points of control. We discuss them serially.

A change in membrane tension produced by increasing the force in the syringeal muscles, all other factors remaining constant, will increase frequency and at the same time will increase the cross-section of the constricted passage—the mean value of "d" (figures 103, 107). As "d" increases from a very small value, the amplitude of vibration will increase, hence an increase in frequency will be associated with an increase in acoustical amplitude. As "d" continues to increase, and membrane tension continues to rise, a point of maximum amplitude will be reached, beyond which the available forces in the flowing air stream can no longer stimulate the membrane to vibrate through the amplitude range permitted by the size of the passage "d." As "d" increases beyond this point the acoustically significant pulsating air flow will decrease, and the acoustically inert nonpulsating air flow will increase, with the result that acoustical amplitude will *decrease* as frequency increases. In summary, changes in membrane tension produce simultaneously a change both in frequency and amplitude. In the low frequency range the "coupling" will be direct, i.e., frequency and amplitude will rise together. Above a transition frequency the "coupling" will be inverse, i.e., amplitude will fall as frequency rises.

It is a characteristic of the songs of most of the Oscines that muscle tension will oscillate within a particular phrase, producing a rapid modulation in both frequency and amplitude about mean values. The low mass of the syringeal muscles permits relatively high values for the modulating frequency, approaching 400 c/s, and within the modulating period frequency/amplitude coupling may be direct or inverse, depending on the "carrier" or mean frequency of the modulation. Many examples of such modulations are shown in chapter 8.

A change in sac pressure, all other factors remaining unchanged, may produce two opposing effects. There will be an increased pressure drop across the constricted passage which, for a constant value of "d," would increase air flow, hence acoustical amplitude. Simultaneously the increased sac pressure will force the membrane farther into the bronchial lumen, thereby decreasing the cross-sectional area at "d" with an associated decrease in acoustical amplitude. I do not have sufficient data to determine the resultant of these two effects. It is, however, possible that the axis of the bowed membrane will *not* be perpendicular to the bronchial axis but will be bent downstream by increasing pressure on the lung side of the syrinx. If this happens, and I think it probable, increasing the sac pressure would always be associated with an increase in acoustical amplitude, without simultaneously affecting the frequency of membrane vibration.

Finally there is the external labium which has, according to Setterwall, associated musculature which permits its insertion into or withdrawal from the bronchial lumen. This would provide a method for varying the cross-sectional area at "d," hence for varying signal amplitude without an associated change in frequency. We have seen in chapter 8 a number of examples in which amplitude changes substantially, without an associated frequency change. These manifestations could be explained either by an assumed variation in sac pressure, or by the proposed function of the external labium. The rapidity with which such pure amplitude modulations occurs would point to motion of the external labium as the source since the mass of the sac system is in all probability too large to permit such rapid amplitude fluctuations.

We have considered so far the case in which the tympanic membranes are free to vibrate sinusoidally, giving rise to what we have called "whistled" song with negligible harmonic content. For each avian species there is a threshold frequency below which harmonics appear, the number of the dominant harmonic increasing as fundamental frequency decreases below the threshold value. This threshold frequency is associated with a membrane tension sufficiently low to cause the vibrating membrane to be constrained as it approaches the opposing bronchial wall, thus departing from a purely sinusoidal vibration, and giving rise to harmonics of the fundamental frequency.

As the fundamental frequency crosses the threshold value, the second harmonic appears, rising in amplitude as the fundamental frequency decreases, with a simultaneous drop in the relative amplitude of the *fundamental*. As the fundamental frequency falls still further, with relaxation of muscle tension, the third harmonic appears and increases in amplitude, with a decrease in the relative amplitude of the *second* harmonic. The process continues as muscle tension and fundamental frequency decline with dominance of harmonics of successively higher number.

The process can be visualized as a rippling of the vibrating membrane, the period of the ripple corresponding to the frequency of the dominant harmonic, the frequency of the fundamental controlled by muscle tension. The same controls are available as for whistled song. Muscle tension dictates the fundamental frequency and, all other factors remaining unchanged, the number of the dominant harmonic. An increase in sac pressure increases signal amplitude and also changes the character of the harmonic spectrum. A change in position of the external labium will change the value of the threshold frequency below which harmonics appear; the greater its penetration into the bronchial lumen, the higher the threshold frequency, and vice versa.

It is apparent that any Oscine must have the ability to sing in either the whistled or harmonic domains. Many birds elect one or the other for their songs and calls; some will use both. Crows, for example, appear to limit themselves to the harmonic domain as do the white- and red-breasted nuthatches. The wood thrush on the other hand appears to restrict itself to whistled song. The black-capped chickadee sings a whistled song but its scold phrases are in the harmonic domain. Mockingbird and brown thrasher appear to wander between whistled phrases and phrases with substantial harmonic content almost at random.

In neither the whistled nor the harmonic domain is there evidence for tracheal modulation of the source-generated sound. Even in the calls of cranes and swans, whose very long tracheae are partly coiled within the breast cavity, there is no sign of tracheal modulation. And for the myna, the most accomplished of the talking birds, the evidence also shows that the sounds generated at the source are not modulated in the trachea. As shown in chapter 6, absence of tracheal modulation is almost certainly due to a matching of the impedance of source and trachea, producing a situation in which the combination acts as a tube partially closed at one end and open at the other, thus permitting the source-generated signal to traverse the trachea without modification.

Turning now to the two acoustical sources, chapter 5 presents many examples in which birds from diverse families sing two harmonically unrelated notes or phrases simultaneously. Had we been able to devise techniques for separating two phrases close together in mean frequency, or for separating overlapping glissandi, we could have produced a great many more. It seems likely that use of the two acoustical sources is a common, not an exceptional occurrence in the songs of most birds. Here also is clear proof that the trachea is without modulating effect since tracheal control would effectively inhibit the appearance of two simultaneous signals.

We note that the two acoustical sources may both operate in the whistled domain, in the harmonic domain, or may simultaneously produce one signal which is whistled and one with substantial harmonic content (see for example the catbird phrase, figure 52). We conclude that the two sources are completely independent with the possible exception that the maximum acoustic amplitude attainable when one source alone is operating may not be attainable when the air flowing from the lungs is divided between two sources.

Before leaving the Oscines we should consider the steps involved in making the transition from normal respiration to song. I have been able to find nothing in the literature dealing with this transition, hence what follows must be taken as speculation. It has been shown that pressure in the sac system is an essential precursor to song; and it seems clear that such pressures cannot be generated if syrinx and trachea can discharge air freely from the lungs. We assume then that birds must have a valve or sphincter on the lung side of the syrinx which can be closed while pressure is built up in the interclavicular sac. That rise in pressure will force the relaxed tympaniform membrane into the bronchial lumen, thus closing the passages through bronchi, trachea, and oral cavity. If one source only is to be used the muscles associated with the other are relaxed and that passage will remain closed. The other muscles are placed in tension, creating a constricted passage in the appropriate bronchus, and song begins. When the two sources are used simultaneously, both sets of muscles will be in tension, creating two constricted passages. When song ceases, the sac pressure is released through appropriate muscle action, the syringeal muscles are also relaxed, and respiration proceeds normally.

Turning from the Oscines to the more primitive families we encounter, according to the anatomists, a simplification of the syringeal structure. The Tyrannidae, for example, are said to have one, sometimes two, pairs of intrinsic syringeal muscles as compared with five or more pairs for the Oscines. The external labium may be present or absent. We have seen in Rüppell's description of the herring gull syrinx that this species has no external labium, and no intrinsic syringeal muscles (in the sense that these muscles originate and terminate in the syrinx). The statement has been made that the "complexity" of the song increases with increasing proliferation of syringeal musculature. I can find no evidence which would support this hypothesis.

If "complexity" is defined as a phrase or song with elaborate modulations, then the Tyrannidae phrases are quite as complex as those characteristic of the most accomplished Oscines. Consider, for example, the oscillograms for Traill's flycatcher (figure 26c) and for the eastern kingbird (figure 26b), and compare these phrases with those of the song sparrow (figure 39c) or Lapland longspur (figure 39b). One cannot say that the Oscine phrases are more complex. To be sure the song sparrow has far greater variety in its songs than any of the Tyrannidae, but variety and complexity are not synonymous since a single complex phrase must surely require as elaborate anatomical features as would be needed to produce a number of such phrases.

Consider also the song of the short-billed dowitcher (figure 24a), which matches and even exceeds the "complexity" of many Oscine songs. Similar statements could be made for the western grebe (figure 20b), the Laysan albatross (figure 20c), and even for the little tinamou (figure 109).

It is also evident that not all Oscines sing "complex" songs. The Carolina chickadee, the tufted titmouse, the pygmy nuthatch, and many other oscinine species, have songs much less "complex" than are encountered in other families.

Only one generalization can be made to distinguish the Oscines from the non-Oscine groups; the frequency range for the Oscines is much greater than is encountered elsewhere. The songs of the Laysan albatross and western grebe, in spite of the elaboration of their amplitude envelopes, are sung within a very narrow frequency range. The little tinamou encompasses only a little more than a musical whole tone in its long and elaborate song.

We conclude then that the syringeal embellishments characteristic of the Oscines contribute little more than the ability to sing over a greater frequency range, and even here the presence or absence of intrinsic syringeal muscles may be more important than the number of pairs which are present.

We have discussed three points of control used by the bird in varying its song. Movement of the external labium into and out of the bronchial lumen is one method for varying amplitude without a simultaneous change in frequency, but this can also be accomplished by pressure change in the clavicular sac. Loss of the labium would then impose only a small restriction on song complexity, viz., amplitude could not be modulated as rapidly with the more massive sac system. A reduction in the number of pairs of syringeal muscles is more difficult to interpret. If enough remain to vary membrane tension over a sufficiently wide interval, there should be no loss in song complexity; the vocal performance of the Tyrannidae would appear to support this conclusion. If there are *no* intrinsic syringeal muscles the bird can still sing but its frequency range will be severely restricted. In this case we assume a relatively thick membrane whose tension increases as pressure in the clavicular sac forces it into the bronchial lumen. At some sac pressure (and associated membrane tension) a constricted bronchial passage would be formed and the membrane stimulated to vibrate, but manifestly these conditions could obtain only over a narrow frequency range.

In summary, the bird needs only its membranes and the clavicular sac pressure to permit vocalization; even with these features standing alone a fairly elaborate song can be sung. Additional controls add to the frequency range covered but other effects would appear to be minor.

We have also been able to estimate, for a few oscinine species, the frequency and time discrimination characteristic of these small birds. The validity of the method used depends on the assumption that there is an aural feedback by means of which the bird controls the sung phrases. This assumption is amply supported by Konishi's data on deafened birds. The results would indicate frequency discrimination quite close to human values ($\Delta f/f = 2 - 5 \times 10^{-3}$) and time discrimination of the order $0.3 - 0.5$ msec. This extraordinary time discrimination, perhaps 50 or more times better than values for human ears, indicates that birds hear as such the rapid modulations characteristic of their songs and implies a very large "information content" in even a simple song. It would also account for individual recognition of songs within a given species, through subtleties which human ears cannot perceive.

We turn now to a few generalizations which can be extracted from the songs we have analyzed. The frequency range embraced in the songs of particular species can vary from a musical whole tone or less to a maximum of nearly four full octaves. The greatest range encountered in this study is for the brown-headed cowbird, whose song includes the interval 0.75 to 10.7 kc/s. As indicated earlier the frequency range encountered in bird song is the only characteristic which appears to be related to syringeal anatomy. The Oscines show the greatest frequency range; the range becomes much more limited when intrinsic syringeal muscles are small in number or absent.

The frequency range from species to species is, of course, much greater. The lowest frequency I have noted is for the spruce grouse, which sings a basso profundo at 80–90 c/s. A few other species approach this value; the blue grouse at 100–150 c/s, the great gray owl at about 200 c/s, the American bittern at 200 c/s, and the mourning dove at 500 c/s. At the other end of the scale, the highest frequency encountered is for the "gleee" of the brown-headed cowbird at 10.7 kc/s. Perhaps of greater interest is the blackpoll warbler, whose entire song is sung within the four musical semitones from 8.5 to 10.6 kc/s. On the assumption that the songs studied do indeed embrace the maximum and minimum frequencies, bird songs cover the range 85 to 10,700 c/s, or seven octaves. It is assumed that this range is made possible by a species-specific thickness of the tympaniform membranes. Manifestly no single membrane could be stretched to cover so great a frequency range, hence the postulate of a thick membrane for the grouse, and a very thin one for the blackpoll warbler. We recall also that among the Oscines the threshold for the generation of harmonics ranges upward from 1500 c/s, hence harmonic spectra would be found at all fundamental frequencies below this value. The wave forms for grouse, bittern, owl, and dove are all pure sinusoids, without significant harmonic content. The anomaly can readily be accounted for by variation in membrane thickness. Unhappily there are no thickness values reported in the literature for these membranes, with the single exception of the 6–7 μ value given by Setterwall for a small Oscine.

It is a curious fact that many birds do not make full use of their vocal equipment. The common crow, for example, sings only in the harmonic domain, the wood thrush only whistled songs. The Carolina chickadee sings a single simple song; the song sparrow has 10 to 20 different songs in its repertoire, all different and each containing phrases of great complexity and even greater diversity. The varied thrush sings a monotonous song containing a few sustained notes; the mockingbird will sing for hours without duplicating his varied phrases. I have no pat explanation to offer for this divergence in vocal behavior. Parsimonious Nature does not permit the evolution of functionless attributes in her creatures, and so denies the anthropomorphic conclusion that birds sing for the "joy" of it. I suggest the more tenable hypothesis that virtuosity per se is an isolating mechanism. Certainly the notion that mockingbird, brown thrasher, and catbird, among others, "communicate" for hours at a stretch or that all of the phrases produced by the song sparrow have meaning for his auditors cannot reasonably be supported, unless one is willing to say that birds do indeed "talk" to each other.

There appears to be no correlation between the size of the bird and the mean frequency of its song. I have suggested that the mean frequency is dictated by the thickness of the tympaniform membrane; the thicker the membrane, the lower the frequency. Hence membrane thickness would appear to be a feature subject to independent evolutionary development, not a dimension which automatically follows an increase in the size of the bird.

Finally, I suggest some anatomical and behavioral experiments which might cast additional light on the physiology of avian vocalization, and support or deny the conclusions just summarized.

1. There are data in the literature as to the points of attachment of the intrinsic syringeal muscles but there appear to have been no attempts made to see what functional purpose is served by each muscle pair. Modern anatomical techniques should permit experiments in vitro, perhaps even in vivo, to show precisely how each muscle pair affects the tympanic membranes and associated structures.

2. I have found relatively little in the literature regarding the external labium. A special study of this feature should be worth while, to see how commonly it exists, and whether there is indeed associated musculature permitting its movement within the bronchial lumen.

3. I have postulated thickness of the tympaniform membrane as a species-specific feature. It should be simple to measure membrane thickness for birds varying widely in the mean frequency of their song, thereby determining directly the validity of this hypothesis.

4. I confess to some pessimism as to the possibility of observing directly the physiology of vocalization in a living bird. Perhaps, however, someone will be ingenious enough to devise satisfactory techniques, perhaps involving X-ray cinematography.

5. I have found no studies in the literature dealing with the transition from normal respiration to song or with sac pressures and air velocities during song. Such studies should present no serious experimental difficulties since all that is needed is a small and highly sensitive pressure transducer which the living bird would find unobjectionable. Sac pressure and song could then be recorded simultaneously. An examination of sac pressure as it relates to acoustic amplitudes could not fail to be revealing.

6. I should perhaps register one caveat. Many attempts have been made to develop useful information by blowing through a dissected syrinx and trachea in endeavoring to reproduce sounds made by the living bird. I doubt very much that such experiments can be anything but misleading. As indicated earlier, tracheal modulation is avoided by maintaining a particular ratio between the cross-sectional area of the trachea and that of the constricted passage created by the tympaniform membrane. The chances of setting up the necessary condition with dissected material not subject to the controls available to the living bird would appear to be very slim.

7. I have searched diligently for evidence bearing on tracheal modulation of the source-generated sounds and have concluded that the trachea plays no acoustical role in avian vocalization. This finding can readily be tested experimentally. It would be necessary only to persuade an experimental subject to sing in a helium-oxygen atmosphere. Since the velocity of sound is higher in helium-oxygen than in air, the tracheal resonances would increase correspondingly, and the effect on a song or call in the harmonic domain should be readily observable. If no effect is observed, we have conclusive proof that tracheal resonances do not influence vocalization. Ideally one should select a bird having a stereotyped song or call within the harmonic domain,

viz., a white- or red-breasted nuthatch, a black-capped chickadee (scold), or perhaps a myna taught to speak a particular phrase. If such a bird were in a cage in a sealed container through which air, or the helium-oxygen mixture were allowed to flow, the change in environment could be made gradually, without undue disturbance. A microphone in the cage would permit the necessary recordings to be made with ease, and without distortion.

The velocity of sound in air at 20°C and atmospheric pressure is 1130 ft/sec; in a mixture comprising 80% helium, 20% oxygen it is 2120 ft/sec. Tracheal resonance frequencies will be proportional to these velocities; the values for helium-oxygen 1.9 times the values for air. The central frequency in the harmonic spectrum defining the call of the red-breasted nuthatch is 2500 c/s. If the spectrum is controlled by tracheal resonance, the value should rise to near 5000 c/s in a helium-oxygen atmosphere. A change to a helium-oxygen atmosphere might produce a small effect on the frequency of vibration of the tympanic membrane itself, due to a slight decrease in the loading on the vibrating membrane. Such an effect could hardly exceed a few percent, and would be negligible as compared with the effect on resonance frequencies in the trachea.

8. Finally, it would be interesting to see whether the instrumental technique described here could throw light on those acoustical factors involved in individual recognition. One might attack the problem by selecting a species with a simple stereotyped song; for example, the tufted titmouse, the black-capped or the Carolina chickadee. One would record many songs of several individuals, then determine by statistical procedures which qualities, such as mean frequency, amplitude, note duration, varied significantly from individual to individual.

I have found this attempt at acoustical detective work both stimulating and enjoyable. It should be said, however, that all "proofs" presented here are indirect since they involve deductions as to physiological processes based simply on the acoustical features present in the songs. The evidence, to use a legal phrase, is purely circumstantial and must be given less weight than direct experimental proof of the processes involved in avian vocalization.

Had I the deductive powers of an Albert Campion, a Gideon Fell, or any of the other highly erudite detectives of fiction, I might have done better. However convincing the model developed here may be to its author, direct experimental evidence is much to be desired; if this study provides the necessary stimulus, I shall be quite content.

LITERATURE CITED

ALDROVANDUS, Ulyssis Aldrovandi
  1600. Ornithologia. Bononiae.

BEEBE, William
  1925. The variegated Tinamou. Zoologica, vol. 6, no. 2, p. 215.

BELL TELEPHONE LABORATORIES
  1946. Technical aspects of visible speech. Bell Telephone Systems Monograph B-1415.
    Also *in* Journ. Acoust. Soc. America, 1946, vol. 17, pp. 1–89.

BERNDT, R.
  1938. Intrasternale Trachealschlingen bei Vögeln. Morph. Jahrb., vol. 82, pp. 69, 113.

BORROR, Donald J., and REESE, Carl R.
  1956. Vocal gymnastics in Wood Thrush songs. Ohio Journ. Sci., vol. 56, pp. 177–182.

COUES, Elliott
  1903. Key to North American Birds, vol. 2.

CUVIER, G.
  1805. Leçons d'Anatomie comparée, vol. 6, pp. 462, 491.

FANT, Gunnar
  1960. Acoustic theory of speech production, pp. 109, 126. Mouton & Co. 's–Gravenhage.

FORBUSH, E. H.
  1925. Birds of Massachusetts and other New England States. Mass. Dept. Agric., vol. 1,
    p. 317.

FÜRBRINGER, Max
  1888. Untersuchungen zur Morphologie und Systematik der Vögel, II: Allgemeine
    Theil. Amsterdam.

GARROD, A. H.
  1876. On some anatomical characters which bear upon the major divisions of the pas-
    serine birds, Part 1. Proc. Zool. Soc. London, 1876, p. 506, 5 pls.

GRÜTZNER, P.
1879. Physiologie der Stimme und Sprache. *In* Hermann, Handbuch der Physiologie der Bewegungsapparate, vol. 1, no. 2, pp. 144. Leipzig.

HÄCKER, Valentin
1900. Der Gesang der Vögel. Jena. Gustav Fischer.

HÉRISSANT, M.
1753. Recherches sur les organes de la voix des quadrupèdes et de celle des oiseaux. Academie Roy. Sci. Mem., pp. 279–295.

HUXLEY, Thomas Henry
1871. A Manual of the Anatomy of Vertebrated Animals, p. 103. London.

JOOS, Martin
1948. Acoustic phonetics. Journ. Ling. Soc. America, vol. 24, no. 2, suppl. April–June, pp. 1–137.

KNECHT, Sigrid
1940. Über den Gehörsinn und die Musikalität der Vögel. Zeitschr. vergl. Physiol., vol. 27, pp. 169–232.

KONISHI, Masakazu
1964. Effects of deafening on song development in two species of Juncos. The Condor, vol. 66, pp. 85–102.
1965. The role of auditory feedback in the control of vocalization in the White-Crowned Sparrow. Zeitschr. Tierpsychologie, vol. 22, pp. 770–783.

KORTRIGHT, Francis H.
1942. The ducks, geese and swans of North America, p. 69. Stackpole.

MILNE-EDWARDS, H.
1876. Leçons sur la Physiologie et l'Anatomie comparée de l'homme et des Animaux, vol. 12, p. 623.

MISKIMEN, Mildred
1961. Sound Production in passerine birds. The Auk, vol. 68, pp. 493–504.

MÜLLER, Johannes
1845. Über bisher Unbekannte typische Verschiedenheiten der Stimmorgane der Passerinen. Abh. Königl. Akad. Wiss zu Berlin. [Translated by F. Jeffrey Bell, Oxford, Clarendon Press, 1878.]

PETERSON, Roger Troy
1947. A field guide to the birds, 2nd ed., p. 216.

PIERCE, John R., and DAVID, Edward E.
1958. Man's world of sound. Doubleday & Co.

POTTER, RALPH K.; KOPP, George A.; and GREEN, Harriet C.
1947. Visible speech. D. Van Nostrand Co. (Reprint: 1966, Dover Publications Inc., New York.)

PUMPHREY, R. J.
1961. Sensory Organs: Hearing. *In* A. J. Marshall, Biology and Comparative Physiology of Birds, vol. 2, ch. 15, pp. 69–86. Academic Press.

RÉTHI, L.
1908. Untersuchungen über die Stimme der Vögel, Abt. III: Anatomie und Physiologie des Menschen und der Tiere sowie Theoretische Medizin. Sitzungsberichte Acad. Wiss. Wien, Math-naturwiss. Klasse, vol. 117, pp. 93–109.

Rüppel, Werner
   1933. Physiologie und Akustik der Vögelstimme. Jour. Ornithologie, vol. 74 [LXXXI, vol. 3] pp. 433–542.

Savart, M. Felix
   1826. Memoire sur la voix des oiseaux. Ann. chimie physique, ser. 2, vol. 32, pp. 5–24, 113–130. Paris.

Setterwall, Carl G.
   1901. Studier öfver Syrinx hos *Polymyoda passeres*. Dissertation, University of Lund.

Shower, E. G. and Biddulph, R.
   1931. Differential pitch sensitivity of the ear. Journ. Acoust. Soc. America, vol. 3, pp. 275–287.

Small, Arnold M.
   1937. An Objective Analysis of Artistic Violin Performance. Iowa State Mus., vol. 4 (1937), pp. 172–231. [Not seen.] Also *in* Carl E. Seashore, The Psychology of Music, 1938, p. 204. McGraw-Hill.

Thorpe, W. H.
   1959. Talking birds and the mode of action of the vocal apparatus of birds. Proc. Zool. Soc. London, vol. 132, pp. 441–455.
   1961. Bird Song. Cambridge University Press, p. 112.

Appendix 1   ALPHABETICAL LIST OF BIRD NAMES

American bittern, *Botaurus lentiginosus*
American golden plover, *Pluvialis dominica*
American goldfinch, *Spinus tristis*
American woodcock, *Philohela minor*

Barred owl, *Strix varia*
Bewick's wren, *Thryomanes bewickii*
Black-bellied tree duck, *Dendrocygna autumnalis*
Black-capped chickadee, *Parus atricapillus*
Blackpoll warbler, *Dendroica striata*
Black-throated blue warbler,
   Dendroica caerulescens
Blue grosbeak, *Guiraca caerulea*
Blue grouse, *Dendragapus obscurus*
Blue jay, *Cyanocitta cristata*
Blue-gray gnatcatcher, *Polioptila caerulea*
Blue-winged warbler, *Vermivora pinus*
Blyth's reed warbler, *Acrocephalus dumetorum*
Brambling, *Fringilla montifringilla*
Broad-winged hawk, *Buteo platypterus*
Brown creeper, *Certhis familiaris*
Brown thrasher, *Toxostoma rufum*
Brown-headed cowbird, *Molothrus ater*
Budgeriger, *Melopsittacus undulatus*
Bullfinch, *Pyrrhula pyrrhula*
Burrowing owl, *Speotyto cunicularia*

California quail, *Lophortyx californicus*
Canada goose, *Branta canadensis*
Cardinal, *Richmondena cardinalis*

Carolina chickadee, *Parus carolinensis*
Carrion crow, *Corvus corone*
Catbird, *Dumetella carolinensis*
Chaffinch, *Fringilla coelebs*
Chalk-browed mockingbird, *Mimus saturninus*
Chestnut-sided warbler, *Dendroica pensylvanica*
Chipping sparrow, *Spizella passerina*
Common crow, *Corvus brachyrhynchos*
Common loon, *Gavia immer*
Common redpoll, *Acanthus flammea*
Common teal, *Anas crecca*
Connecticut warbler, *Oporornis agilis*
Cooper's hawk, *Accipiter cooperii*
Crossbill, *Loxia curvirostra*

Dickcissel, *Spiza americana*
Dunlin, *Erolia alpina*

Eared grebe, *Podiceps caspicus*
Eastern bluebird, *Sialia sialis*
Eastern kingbird, *Tyrannus tyrannus*
Eastern phoebe, *Sayornis phoebe*
European blackbird, *Turdus merula*
European widgeon, *Anas penelope*

Ferruginous owl, *Glaucidium brasilianum*

Garden warbler, *Sylvia borin*
Golden eagle, *Aquila chrysaetos*
Golden-crowned kinglet, *Regulus satrapa*
Golden-winged warbler, *Vermivora chrysoptera*

Grasshopper sparrow,
  Ammodramus savannarum
Grasshopper warbler, *Locustella naevia*
Gray hawk, *Buteo nitidus*
Gray jay, *Perisoreus canadensis*
Gray-cheeked thrush, *Hylocichla minima*
Great gray owl, *Strix nebulosa*
Greater yellowlegs, *Totanus melanoleucus*
Green jay, *Cyanocorax yncas*

Harris' sparrow, *Zonotrichia querula*
Hawk-owl, *Surnia ulula*
Herring gull, *Larus argentatus*
Horned lark, *Eremophila alpestris*
House sparrow, *Passer domesticus*
House wren, *Troglodytes aedon*

Icterine warbler, *Hippolais icterina*
Indian hill myna, *Gracula religiosa*
Indigo bunting, *Passerina cyanea*

Killdeer, *Charadrius vociferus*
Kiskadee flycatcher, *Pitangus sulphuratus*

Lapland longspur, *Calcarius lapponicus*
Laysan albatross, *Diomedea immutabilis*
Leach's petrel, *Oceanodroma leucorhoa*
LeConte's sparrow, *Passerherbulus caudacutus*
Lesser whitethroat, *Sylvia curruca*
Lesser yellowlegs, *Totanus flavipes*
Little nightjar, *Caprimulgus parvulus*
Little tinamou, *Crypturellus soui*
Loggerhead shrike, *Lanius ludovicianus*
Long-billed curlew, *Numenius americanus*
Long-eared owl, *Asio otus*

Magpie, *Pica pica*
Mallard, *Anas platyrhynchos*
Marsh tit, *Parus palustris*
Mockingbird, *Mimus polyglottos*
Mourning dove, *Zenaidura macroura*

Naked-throated bellbird, *Procnias nudicollis*
Nightingale, *Luscinia megarhynchos*

Oilbird, *Steatornis caripensis*
Orchard oriole, *Icterus spurius*
Oregon junco, *Junco oreganus*
Osprey, *Pandion haliaetus*

Palm warbler, *Dendroica palmarum*
Parula warbler, *Parula americana*
Pied flycatcher, *Ficedula hypoleuca*
Pied-billed grebe, *Podilymbus podiceps*

Prairie warbler, *Dendroica discolor*
Prothonotary warbler, *Protonotaria citrea*
Purple finch, *Carpodacus purpureus*
Pygmy nuthatch, *Sitta pygmaea*

Rattling cisticola, *Cisticola chiniana*
Red-breasted nuthatch, *Sitta canadensis*
Red-necked grebe, *Podiceps grisegena*
Red-shafted flicker, *Colaptes cafer*
Red-shouldered hawk, *Buteo lineatus*
Red-throated loon, *Gavia stellata*
Redwinged blackbird, *Agelaius phoeniceus*
Robin, *Turdus migratorius*
Rock wren, *Salpinctes obsoletus*
Rough-legged hawk, *Buteo lagopus*
Ruby-crowned kinglet, *Regulus calendula*

Sage grouse, *Centrocercus urophasianus*
Savi's warbler, *Locustella luscinioides*
Screech owl, *Otus asio*
Seaside sparrow, *Ammospiza maritima*
Short-billed dowitcher, *Limnodromus griseus*
Slate-colored junco, *Junco hyemalis*
Smooth-billed ani, *Crotophaga ani*
Song sparrow, *Melospiza melodia*
Spruce grouse, *Canachites canadensis*
Starling, *Sturnus vulgaris*
Summer tanager, *Piranga rubra*
Swamp sparrow, *Melospiza georgiana*

Tennessee warbler, *Vermivora peregrina*
Townsend's solitaire, *Myadestes townsendi*
Traill's flycatcher, *Empidonax traillii*
Tree pipit, *Anthus trivialis*
Tree swallow, *Iridoprocne bicolor*
Trumpeter swan, *Olor buccinator*
Tufted titmouse, *Parus bicolor*
Turtle dove, *Streptopelia turtur*

Varied thrush, *Ixoreus naevius*
Variegated tinamou, *Crypturellus variegatus*
Vesper sparrow, *Pooecetes gramineus*

Western grebe, *Aechmophorus occidentalis*
Western meadowlark, *Sturnella neglecta*
Whip-poor-will, *Caprimulgus vociferus*
Whistling swan, *Olor columbianus*
White-breasted nuthatch, *Sitta carolinensis*
White-crowned manakin, *Pipra pipra*
White-crowned sparrow,
  Zonotrichia leucophrys
White-eyed vireo, *Vireo griseus*
White-necked thrush, *Turdus albicollis*

White-winged junco, *Junco aikeni*
Whooping crane, *Grus americana*
Wood thrush, *Hylocichla mustelina*

Yellow warbler, *Dendroica petechia*
Yellow-breasted chat, *Icteria virens*
Yellow-shafted flicker, *Colaptes auratus*

The following references were used to derive the taxonomic and common names of the species listed.

American Ornithologists' Union
    1957. Check-list of North American Birds, fifth edition.
Delacour, Jean
    1951. Waterfowl of the World.
De Schauensee, R. M.
    1966. The species of birds of South America with their distribution.
Mackworth-Praed, C. W., and Grant, C. H. B.
    1955. Birds of eastern and north eastern Africa.
Ripley, S. D.
    1961. Synopsis: Birds of India and Pakistan.
Serventy, D. L., and Whittell, H. M.
    1948. Birds of western Australia.
Vaurie, Charles
    1959. The birds of the Palearctic fauna: Passeriformes.
    1965. The birds of the Palearctic fauna: Non-Passeriformes.

Appendix 2 INSTRUMENTAL MODIFICATIONS

Several of the instruments previously described have been modified, more or less extensively, to meet the requirements of this investigation. The modifications have been made by Mr. Paul C. Hoell of the Du Pont Company's Central Research Department. There follow descriptions of these modifications, provided by Mr. Hoell, stated in such terms that any qualified manufacturer could supply the modified instruments.

Mr. Hoell has also supplied a more detailed description of the high and low pass sharply cutting filters and of the hum reject filter, which are not commercially available.

Oscilloscope

Equivalent to Tektronix Model RM-304, except:

The amplified "vertical" signal channel, at a point beyond the vertical gain control, is capacitively coupled to an output terminal through a low impedance (cathode follower) driver.

Dual Preset Timer

Equivalent to Beckman Model 6005 Dual Preset Accumulator, except:

An internal, crystal-controlled, 100 kc/s oscillator is added and permanently connected to the counter input through a bistable gate. The count is started by an external trigger pulse ($\pm$ 1 v, minimum) and stopped by an internal reset pulse.

Counter capacity: Six-digit decade.

Setting range: 0–10 sec to 10 μsec intervals.

N_1 output (coincident with first count setting) consists of a $+20$ v, 1 μsec rise, 10 μsec single pulse and a 50 msec relay contact closure.

N_2 output (coincident with second count setting) consists of a $+20$ v, 50 μsec square pulse and resets both the counter and the input gate. Reset time: less than 20 μsec.

Period Counter

Equivalent to Hewlett-Packard Model 5532A Electronic Counter, except:

The counting operation is normally inhibited by a monostable gate. An externally applied "arming" pulse ($+20$ v, 1 μsec rise, 10 μsec duration) initiates a 100 msec enabling period.

The counter measures the interval between the first and second (or first and eleventh, etc., as selected) successive, positive-going zero-crossover of the input signal to occur during the armed period.

The counter is automatically reset after an adjustable "hold" interval.

Filters

The variable-filter system consists of a number of decade inductors and capacitors interconnected as shown in figure 6. The performance of the low pass filter is shown on figure 7; that of the high pass filter is identical. In the following tabulation co-efficients are given for the circuit elements. When multiplied by p (the reciprocal of the cut-off frequency in seconds per cycle) values of inductance are obtained in henries, of capacitance in microfarads. The filter is designed to operate from a 5600 ohm source into a 5600 ohm load.

Circuit Element	Low-Pass	High-Pass
A	410.0	24.91
B	1214.	16.58
C	48.71	1938.
D	11.19	654.4
E	32.43	16.91
F	47.77	72.19
G	410.0	19.47
H	1783.	16.58
J	48.71	445.6
K	41.49	1938.

Decade inductors, such as Aerovox Series ALD or Sprague Series 850 WA, and decade capacitors such as Aerovox Series ACD, are suitable for constructing these filters.

The hum reject filter, passing frequencies above approximately 300 c/s, is shown at the right of figure 6. It is assembled using standard fixed-value components available from any electronics supply shop.